John Walker Pattison was born on Monday, 4th February 1957 to parents John and Ruby. He has lived most of his years in the wonderful seaside town of South Shields, and enjoyed an uneventful, but happy childhood, and he loved to seek out trouble.

Today, Pattison enjoys being the practical joker, especially with his grandchildren. He openly admits to spending his school days clowning around, and neglected his intellectual chemistry, subsequently leaving school with a handful of worthless qualifications.

In 1973, he started work in a local shipyard until the spectre of cancer gripped his future in a deathly stranglehold. What happened next is his unique story, his *Memoirs of a Cancer Survivor*.

To the Oglala Lakota Sioux Nation, who unknowingly supported my psychological instability, providing untold inspiration during my most difficult times.

My wife June, not until fate brought us together did I discover who I truly was.

Donna Julie Pattison, your fight was my fight, and my success was your success. We overcame the odds together.

My family, and friends, both here and across the Atlantic Ocean - nothing is as important as family.

Space rock legends, Hawkwind – your music will always resonate in the canyons of my inner soul.

# JOHN WALKER PATTISON

## ME AND MY SHADOW
### MEMOIRS OF A CANCER SURVIVOR

AUSTIN MACAULEY PUBLISHERS™
LONDON · CAMBRIDGE · NEW YORK · SHARJAH

A CIP catalogue record for this title is available from the British Library.

ISBN 9781398484597 (Paperback)
ISBN 9781398484603 (Hardback)
ISBN 9781398484610 (ePub e-book)

www.austinmacauley.com

First Published 2022
Austin Macauley Publishers Ltd®
1 Canada Square
Canary Wharf
London
E14 5AA

Mam, dad, and my wonderful sister Allyson – we made a great team.

My grandchildren – Courtney, Kieran, Olivia, Daniel, and Noah. Diane Ward, Jon Corbett, and all of the individuals whom I have had the honour and privilege of caring for during my career in Oncology and Haematology.

To all the nurses and doctors caring for cancer patients the world over, I salute you.

# Chapter 1
# The Irony of Reflection

On a typically cold and dark February night, only weeks before the nation plunged into its first lockdown—due to the Covid-19 pandemic. I thought of my future, my past and my pride of thirty-two years as a nurse working in the demanding field of cancer services. The thought of my grandchildren, a happy marriage and, ultimately, how sweet life was at that moment.

I raised my glass and took another sip of red wine; next to me sat my beautiful wife, June. We were sat in the tastefully decorated 'Cask Lounge', and at the same time, drops of rain were beating against the window, grabbing my attention and drawing my gaze towards the impressive Town Hall building opposite and which had stood there majestically since its completion in 1910 and where we took our wedding vows in 2004.

I sat speechless, mesmerised like never before, reflecting on my decades gone by; the good memories, the not-so-good times and the downright painful recollections, a time when my future was so uncertain.

How ironic, or was it just a strange twist of fate, that forty-five years ago I stood right here, under very different circumstances, battling a crippling illness that threatened to rob me of any future.

Back in1975, this was not a public house, but part of the 'Town Hall Garage' selling a range of high-quality cars. At that time, I had a weekend ritual to follow, each Saturday morning, regardless of how I felt, I would take the bus ride to the garage, simply to admire and covet the Datsun 280Z that had pride of place in the showroom. The black paintwork gleamed from every conceivable angle, yet at the same time, it reflected my forlorn image.

It was, of course, for sale, although the price tag meant nothing to me—I could not afford it, plain and simple. But it became my iconic motivation—that was, until other, more significant inspirations superseded it. I fantasised about owning that car every time I walked into that showroom and those dreams were important.

I needed an incentive more than ever before, as I tried to come to terms with my illness and a focus that could guide me through the unforgiving ravages of chemotherapy treatment; something that could help me deal with, although on many occasions I failed to deal with the uncompromising side effects of the brutal chemical prescription I was receiving.

Yes, like anyone else, I could dream, but in all honesty, I needed to distance myself from the savage attack that was defeating both my physical and psychological well-being in unison. Each week, I would make the pilgrimage to the 'Town Hall Garage' just to admire this remarkable piece of machinery that realistically was way beyond my reach. It was quite simply escapism, a dream. But, importantly, at that time, it was an essential element of my coping mechanism.

My mind, still to this very day, will drift back to those dark times, subconsciously digging deep within my pockets to uncover repressed thoughts. There were so many difficult days when my mind would be clouded with fear and pessimism, days when my mortality was under threat by a denizen that came out of nowhere and over which I had no control.

Yet, I can at least acknowledge now just how lucky, how fortunate I was to have survived what remains the most feared diagnosis known to society, a cancer diagnosis. Sadly, despite the advances made in treatments today, not everyone will be as fortunate as I have been.

As I lifted the red wine once more to my lips and in the strangest twist of fate, my attention was quickly brought back to the present as the daily National Express London to South Shields bus cruised past. Ironically, only weeks before my ill-fated diagnosis, that very same daily express took me to London and my very first adventure as an adolescent, a trip that would balance me onto the edge of danger.

My dreams, my aspirations and my future would be turned upside down as the diagnosis I did not understand, the diagnosis that was divulged to my parents without my consent or knowledge and which would shape my life in such a way that I could never have imagined. My parents did all they could to shield me from the knowledge that the symptoms I experienced and the investigations I had recently undergone, all came to the same conclusion, cancer.

They decided the best course of action was to keep that information from me. How they planned to do so when I was facing not months but years of chemotherapy and radiotherapy will forever remain a mystery. Whilst I cannot condone their attempted secrecy, I fully understand their desire to protect their only son, as there is no worse feeling in the world than being told that your child has cancer.

I was about to embark on a journey of unrivalled proportions, a pathway that was beyond my comprehension and understanding and more importantly, was beyond my control. Strangely, it would be a journey that would make me the person I am today, perhaps a better person than I might have become had cancer not torn my life to shreds and then influenced my entire future.

I would be taken to the very edge of existence on more than one occasion, I would stare the grim reaper in the face, be delivered to death's door only to find that there was no one at home to take me in. The chemical messengers attacked my body from every conceivable angle in an attempt to rid my body of its unwanted assailant. The poison knew no compassion.

Chemotherapy would snatch my innocence and my naivety leaving me weak, vulnerable and on more than one occasion, ready to submit. I think perhaps the pivotal moment that was instrumental in changing the direction of my life and indeed, my future took place within the confines of a busy cancer ward at Newcastle General Hospital in 1976.

My cancer diagnosis had been established twelve months earlier and the effects of cycle after cycle of chemotherapy that had been pumped into my accommodating veins rendered me completely demoralised by the onslaught of the barbaric medicine. As I saw it, the savagery of chemotherapy and its unrelenting side effects had led to a daily psychological battle that I seemed to be losing.

I had been receiving treatment for more than a year and yet despite my physical and psychological struggle to accept the diagnosis and tolerate the treatment, it had all been in vain as it proved, not for the first time to be unsuccessful and the cancer was progressing. I was emotionally unstable, I felt defeated, completely fatigued, tearful and ready to capitulate I could take no more.

There was only so much one person could take. Like an immature teenager, I felt I had reached my limit; quite simply, I could take no more of this unbiased attack that was beginning to destroy my mind and was eroding my sanity. I had made my decision. I would accept no more treatment and just allow fate to take its course, whatever the consequences of those actions may be.

Deep down I knew what this decision meant as tears rolled down my cheeks and, being at perhaps the lowest point since diagnosis, I momentarily contemplated suicide. But then, in a rational moment, I thought of the consequences that would have on my parents.

A hidden veil of unanswered questions pestered my subconscious mind every hour of every day. Self-posed questions of mortality and survival raised emotions so diverse and unknown to my immature mind and caused such fear that my tentative optimism was indiscriminately cast aside and replaced by indecision and doubt.

Where was my support, who, if anyone, could help when I was dying of cancer? I awoke each morning and went to bed every night with these thoughts, created by an unwanted accomplice. I was fearful of the permanent psychological damage the disease was causing. Aside from the mental distress, chemotherapy had already inflicted pain and indiscriminate harm physically and my fragile seven stone frame was struggling to recover.

Having already endured many months of the unforgiving brutality of chemotherapy and, now, I am told that my cancer has not been halted despite all of that ferocious treatment that I had accepted for almost a year. During chemotherapy, I had struggled both mentally and physically to deal with the persistent barrage of side effects and my inability to accept the uncertainty that goes hand in hand with this cruel cancer diagnosis.

Following my first relapse, I knew my life was balanced on a knife-edge; the persistent temptation of suicide was never far away, luring me towards its irreversible embrace. The conflict that all cancer patients harbour in the remote depths of their minds, the time we all fear had arrived. I was ready to accept the consequences of ending my treatment.

It was a fact that my body was gripped by cancer, which was unwilling to release its deathly stranglehold. I was aware of what the outcome of my action would be, yet paradoxically I was relieved that from somewhere and I have no idea where, I summoned the courage to make that choice, no more chemotherapy. I felt broken, weak and subverted by illness, defeated by my diagnosis, unable to take another step forward on the uneven road of the cancer journey.

It wasn't just the physical destruction caused by a malignant disease that I objected to, it was also the fact that it was eating into my very soul, sowing seeds of doubt within my mind and interfering with every element of my existence. Slowly but surely, it was leaving a permanent and an unseen reminder, a deep, hidden scar and a legacy, which, if I was fortunate enough to survive, would last forever.

A confrontation between me, an immature and terrified teenager and a young Nurse called Syd would be a moment of pivotal change and a defining instance in my young life, a moment that was destined to happen and I believe a consequence of fate. I was young, defiant, confused and angry and once I set my mind to do something, it would be a brave nurse who would attempt to intervene and change that decision, regardless of how well-intentioned their actions were.

However, with true compassion, empathy and a dogged determination not to stand back and watch me throw my life away, Syd did exactly that, intervened. He told me what I already knew, that without the treatment I would die. My tearful counterargument didn't deter him and, eventually, his support, persuasion and understanding led me to reverse my decision not to have more treatment.

His fervent optimism was admirable and yet he did not glory in his success. Had we not had that conversation, the story would have ended here. Instead, it was the beginning of a lifelong cancer journey that would take me through many new and unknown dimensions in my life, a pathway of self-discovery and learning.

As a consequence, my association with cancer would be a unique and unparalleled journey that was destined to influence so many dimensions of not just my life but others along the way. Today, almost fifty years later, it continues to be a significant component in my life; without the cancer experience, I would not be the person I am today; a better person, a philosophical soul, determined to contribute to the ongoing needs of all those affected by the most feared diagnosis known to society, cancer.

My story is intended to be an insight into my challenges, my anxieties and one of the greatest confrontations known to society, the fight against cancer. However, my story is different to many others because it did not just continue to be my fight. Documenting my experience has been cathartic and I sincerely hope reading this account will help others who have been touched in some way, shape or form by the condition in which medical science still has little or no answer.

We all respond in different ways to the pressure and emotions, the fears and the stigma that this disease can elicit and no textbook or professional can tell you what the correct response is. Statistically, there is a one in two chance of being given a cancer diagnosis at some point during a lifetime and the condition probably affects everyone in society to some extent as we all know someone, friend or loved one who has been diagnosed with this feared illness.

This survivorship chronicle is my personal story, my journal of events and coping strategies, the highs and the many lows of my cancer journey and undoubtedly, it will be very different to every other individual who has been touched by cancer. There are no correct or incorrect responses to the brutality that is brought about by a cancer diagnosis, it is very much an individual response and undoubtedly, it will initiate a whole myriad of different and instinctive responses in each person that it affects.

Emotions do not follow a pre-arranged script when attacked by the turmoil of malignant disease. The confusion inflicted on the mind and the desire to rid my body of this unwanted accomplice is one of the hardest issues to deal with. The feelings of helplessness and despair are at times almost constant companions, yet at other times the pleasure and sanctity of life give you an unexpected determination to battle on.

The fear and emotional retribution cancer brought gave me an appreciation of life that would otherwise have been missing, although it took me some time to realise how sweet and important life truly was and remains. At this early point, it would be wrong not to pay tribute and acknowledge the love that I received from my family, my parents and, of course, my dearest sister, Allyson, but also an extended family of aunts and uncles.

In many respects, my diagnosis allowed me to discover myself and appreciate the wonders of every day, but there were times when my anger at the diagnosis meant that I would resent life itself and question, more than once, my very own existence. On more than just an isolated occasion, I would ask myself whether this fight to survive was worth it.

The darkness that lurked in the canyons of my mind, always attempting to befriend me, caused a pathological resentment that was stronger on some days than others. A darkness that offered its cruel hand and, yet thankfully, I did not have the courage or the heart to step forward and grip that handshake, a handshake that would have terminated my life.

14

The trauma of fighting tooth and nail to beat the demon that is cancer has been instrumental in making me who I am today and I make no apologies for repeating this, but there have also been many other experiences that have helped me to discover who I am, whom John Walker Pattison is and has become.

My life to date has, at times, been difficult, but it has also been one of pleasing discovery and I would not, in hindsight, change any of it, apart from the heartache of a failed marriage and the unnecessary retributions it brought. I certainly feel fortunate for the way my life was mapped out by fate and my experiences to date have allowed me to appreciate all that is good and worthwhile in life itself.

Cancer has played a significant part in my life and has presented many difficult, and life-changing challenges but, hard as it is to understand, many positives came from that. It caused me to reflect on what is and what is not relevant in my life and enabled me to recognise the difficulty other individuals face and find the strength, like so many others, to overcome adversity and to look forward to tomorrow.

My story deals with the effects of not only the disease and its treatments, but also its long-term effects and how I cope with the permanent legacy of cancer survivorship, me and my shadow. It is also about the harrowing dilemma I faced as the father of a daughter given the diagnosis of terminal leukaemia. Strangely, I firmly believe that cancer has given me a virtue that would have been absent had the disease not touched my very existence and threatened it more than once.

Life is a privilege for all of us. You cannot put a price on life and health; they are invaluable and precious and deserve to be respected. Sadly, for many people, it's often the onset of an illness or death of a loved one, which brings that into focus. A cancer diagnosis certainly influences your approach to life, your philosophical beliefs and all that you represent and believe. In that respect, I am no doubt like all other cancer patients, reflective, philosophical, grateful and respectful of a condition that society fears more than any other.

However, not everyone affected by cancer will come up with the same answers; all of us, whether a patient, parent, partner or significant other will have a different perspective on the many perplexing challenges that life puts in front of us, the challenges that cancer throws at us, the numerous dilemmas we face and that are instigated by such a disease. In my situation, it was a cancer diagnosis that influenced my opinions and beliefs, and ironically, shaped my future.

It would seem appropriate, therefore, to describe a few of my early encounters, giving an insight into my character and how it was before the spectre of cancer consumed my adolescence and then moulded my personality into what it is today.

The challenges of a cancer diagnosis, both physical and psychological, remain the same today as they did at the time of my diagnosis. But cancer is so much more than a psychological and physical challenge, it is also a challenge financially but importantly, it affects the remainder of your life. For those fortunate enough to survive, then that legacy is ever-present and is now, at last, recognised by the health care establishment as such.

Today, forty-seven years on, I can reflect on my diagnosis, on my survival and how I stared death squarely in the face. I can see the difficult pathway of life that I had to navigate all those decades ago and the melancholy I now feel, yet also a strange sense of catharsis and most importantly, ironically, gratitude at how life has treated me.

Reflecting on the real possibility of an early death at such a young age makes it easier to accept chronic ill health today, ironically, ill health that is a consequence of the salubrious chemotherapy and radiotherapy delivered nearly fifty years ago. Unexpectedly surviving when the medical staff told my parents, I would not. Overcoming all of the odds, I am now humbled to be one of the longest living cancer survivors in the UK today and so, this is my story.

# Chapter 2
# It's Only Rock and Roll

My story began when Ruby and John announced the arrival of their first child, John Walker Pattison on Monday, 4 February 1957. Born in South Shields, a small seaside town nestling on the North East coast of England, my father was a plumber working along the banks of the River Tyne and my mother managed the household as was the tradition at that time – in later years, she would work a number of part-time jobs.

I would be joined 4 years later by a sister, Allyson Mary. My childhood was uneventful and happy. As a youngster, I enjoyed all that life had to offer, football, fishing and finding trouble, the latter being the easiest to achieve and something I excelled at.

But, it was as an independent twelve-year-old, that I went along to my very first football match in September 1969 to watch Newcastle United. Yet, despite the fact, that on that occasion, the team were beaten one-nil against Derby County, my passion had been ignited. I recall handing over my silver coin and pushing my way through the clackerty-clack of the iron turnstiles.

Then, up the concrete stairs to then be greeted by the lush carpet of green turf and the sound of thousands and thousands of Geordies waiting to greet their heroes is something that stays with you forever. Then, the tingle down your spine as the teams march out and the game gets underway. Today, as a season ticket holder, I remain committed to the black and white army, that has delivered so much pleasure and yet, so much frustration over the years.

Like most schoolboys, I had always dreamed of playing football for the black and white magpies, the nickname of Newcastle United. Realistically, however, most of the other boys at school were much better at the game than I would ever be. I did play a handful of games for the school football team and whenever I did, my father would always be there as my main supporter; although more often than not, I would be on the touchline as the shivering substitute.

Despite my eagerness to play and watch football at that early age, music would become an additional source of inspiration. But, not just any music, it was music that would affect my inner soul, influence much of my life and would be a driving force of motivation in my adolescent years. An adolescence that would experience physical trauma, and psychological pain, greater than any work of fiction.

I would describe myself as an animated extrovert, easy-going with an opinion on most things. Philosophical at times but easy to get on with, relaxed and I like to think that I respect the views and opinions of others, even though I don't always agree; if I don't agree, I'll tell you, but importantly I'm not one to hold a grudge, life is too short for that churlish approach. I am very proud of my family and also my hometown, South Shields.

During my early years, music became something of an obsession; it was the focus of my attention, and to the exclusion of most other things, including my education. At the tentative age of fifteen, I discovered a band called Hawkwind that were, in many respects, still in their infancy regarding their development.

The band was formed in the late sixties by a former street busker and they played what was described as 'space rock', which I immediately identified with it. A raw mixture of electronics, guitars and a hypnotic beat of percussion; blended into the musical equation, of an inventive light show with saxophone and an exotic dancer!

It was a Neanderthal approach to music that influenced the way so many other bands deliver their music and continue to do so even today. The band played many venues the length and breadth of the country and many of these gigs were free shows, often supporting worthy charitable causes. Sadly for me, however, a young fifteen-year-old, I had to be content with their records and the regular news articles in the national music journals.

I did not, at that particular juncture in time, realise just how influential and motivational Hawkwind would become as my health deteriorated and how they would unknowingly support me through a psychological battle unlike any other. I would go on to need other motivational influences at different times in my life, some as dependable as Hawkwind and some, far more so.

My association with the band would not be some trivial adolescent preoccupation, far from it. During the many episodes of depression and during the times when I couldn't manage the side effects of the aggressive chemotherapy and the mind-numbing struggle to cope with the real potential of confronting an early death, I would turn to the music of Hawkwind and the escapism it delivered.

In my formative years, I would be the first to admit that my school years were wasted. I did not study as I should have and treated my education as a trivial escapade. Life is there to be enjoyed and I felt education was getting in the way of my enjoyment of life. My best friend at the time, Alan Robertson, known as Robbo, was just as crazy as I was.

If we weren't at one another's house watching such comedy greats as Spike Milligan or Monty Python's Flying Circus; then we'd be preparing to play some outlandish practical joke on friends, much to their disgust and often anger. Classmates would avoid us when we were seen together, knowing that we aimed to create pranks that gave us so much satisfaction.

Robbo and I both enjoyed our music and like so many, it was always our intention to become rock stars and true to this lifestyle, I had been letting my hair grow for some time; this would be my statement, my identity, my freedom; in part, my rebellion.

In 1972, a year when The New Seekers and Donny Osmond would both top the charts, life was all about music for me, but not pop music, space rock was my chosen genre. At night, five or six of us would meet after school and quite innocently walk the streets listening to our music on a cassette player. It was harmless entertainment and it kept us out of trouble.

Thursday and Friday nights were youth club nights. At St Hilda's, while most Friday nights, there would be a disco and occasionally a live band. The youth club was an excellent place to network, but the good thing about these discos was that around 9 p.m. the DJ would play a rock slot with around half a dozen well-established rock tracks, such as Deep Purple, Black Sabbath and Led Zeppelin.

Occasionally, I would convince the disc jockey to play a Hawkwind track, when they did, it would almost always be Silver Machine as this had been a huge chart success for the band, peaking at number three—once I heard the tell-tale sound of its introduction, I would bounce onto the dance floor.

Most often, there would only be a couple of us who would venture onto the dance floor during the rock session; although occasionally, a couple of the girls might also join in, their motivation was one of pure ridicule. Nothing would have stopped me from dancing once Hawkwind was playing, as I saw my attempts at creative dance as a tribute to the band I now revered.

During that time I met Dave, a dedicated Status Quo fan and he also felt that when his band played, he should be there on the dance floor. Subsequently, each Friday, once the rock session was underway, we would seek each other out as if we had a secret mission to accomplish, dancing. Dave became a lifelong dependable friend and I was honoured to be his best man, not once but twice.

There were many anecdotal stories about those early days and the mischief I regularly found, most often of course, I didn't have to look far for it, trouble seemed as though it could find me easily. Having previously admitted to wasting my school years, I subsequently left school with a handful of worthless qualifications.

In later years, I would make up for this lack of educational ambition, after having learned some valuable lessons about life. It had always been my ambition to follow my father into plumbing but due to my poor exam achievements, I was unlikely to be offered an apprenticeship in that trade.

As a young man, I admit to being rather immature and I think this was almost certainly a legacy of my wasted schooling, although I would make up for this later on in life. I do believe that fate governs our lives when we are born, that we are dealt a hand of cards and we have no option other than to play that hand of cards in the game known as life.

That's putting things simply; of course, I do not believe that you can change your fate, call it destiny if you like; although you can tempt fate by your actions. I firmly believe that life is mapped out for us all. I believe my fate was mapped out and being a scholar in those early days was not part of it.

Sometime towards the end of August 1973, my father and I headed across to the North-side of the River Tyne, where interviews were being held for apprenticeships in a number of the local shipyards. Shipbuilding and coal mining had been the mainstay of employment in the area for many decades.

The River Tyne has always been recognised as the world capital of Shipbuilding, having produced quality and famous ships for centuries, including the first of the super tankers, naval vessels by the score, including HMS Ark Royal and Illustrious. Sadly, today, that industry in the North East has almost all but disappeared. During my interview, I sat nervously, fidgeting from side to side.

The interviewer sat quietly, checking out the meagre qualifications that I had proudly presented to him, before offering me an apprenticeship as a Welder. I was quite naive but also bewildered as to why I could not be a plumber, but realising that I had to map out a career of some description and secure a financial future for myself, I accepted the apprenticeship.

It was better than nothing and the pay wasn't too bad, which was an important issue. Dad had explained the necessity of taking up such a post and I respected his view; therefore, in a few moments the indentures were signed. I was on the first rung of the employment ladder, what an ascent that would turn out to be.

And so it was that I had secured my first position of employment and the prospect of life as a Welder. The first twelve-month were spent in a training school starting only a few weeks later. My first pay packet of £9.97 filled me with excitement, as I now could realise one of my very first dreams, to see Hawkwind live.

Late in 1973, Sound's music paper advertised what for me would be an exceptional event, the next Hawkwind tour, just what I had desperately been waiting for. To my great disappointment I found, on closer scrutiny of their tour dates, that there was no Newcastle gig, even though they were playing just about every other corner of the country.

I was determined not to miss an opportunity to see them, so there was only one thing for it, if they were not to visit the North East, then I would have to travel elsewhere to see them. Subsequently, I decided to see them at the now legendary Edmonton Sundown in London early in the New Year of 74.

On my return from work that night I sent off my postal order and a stamped addressed envelope for the most important ticket of my life; the life that would take so many twists and turns, deliver so much heartache and yet provide untold experiences, both good and bad.

My ticket duly arrived and I recall with crystal clarity, just gazing at the maroon coloured ticket before leaving for work on that November morning. I could hardly believe that on 26 January 1974, I would, at last, get to see Hawkwind live and my first encounter with the big city. The experience of working life in the training school revealed many new dimensions of social activity.

A number of the other apprentices had girlfriends and amazed me with some of their tales and escapades. It just proved to demonstrate my innocence and naivety and that I had lots to learn, not only about girls but also about life in general. However, girls were never high on my agenda, like most young lads I'd had some girlfriends, but only one proved serious for me and that was Lauren, the Mayor's daughter.

I fell in love with her the first time I set eyes upon her. I summoned the courage to ask her out, though not personally, as that was too embarrassing. Instead, one of the guys asked her on my behalf and I was amazed when she said yes. Sadly, after a brief courtship, she ended the relationship, which broke my heart into a thousand pieces.

My youthful looks would at times prove a hindrance. Seldom, if at all, could I walk into a bar and get served without being questioned about my age and the legality of being in there, which of course was embarrassing. Therefore, it would be a matter of slipping into the corner and out of sight of the landlord and passing my cash to someone else to get my drinks.

The very first time I recall doing this, was in the Albemarle in 1973, a popular bar in South Shields town centre. I crept into the corner of the room and handed over my fifty pence to Alan, enough for four pints of Newcastle Exhibition beer. I felt like a man and also one of the crowd, but at the end of the night, I was so drunk that I could barely walk and found myself staggering to and fro as if marching across the deck of a ship in a gale-force ten.

'Get the fool into a taxi' was the call from one of the guys. Once home, despite my drunken stupor, I recall stumbling across the doorway only to be faced with the mammoth task of ascending the stairs. I was up three steps and back down two until eventually collapsing on top of my bed; the horrendous experience of the room spinning before I dropped off to sleep and waking the next morning with the hangover from hell.

My first thought was, never again, something most of us have said before, not until the next time that is. Though they never said anything, I'm sure my parents knew that I was drunk, they just do, don't they?

Life in a shipyard brought many more friends and many more adventures. I was a typical teenager, dabbling in all that teenagers do, which included my first experience of cannabis and acid (LSD), after all, it was the acid-drenched seventies. I was never into the drug scene heavily but in an honest account of the influential changes I have experienced, I would admit it did play a small part and I do not intend to hide or falsify any aspect of what is written here.

The time had come to make my long-awaited trip to London and the following week I made the eight-hour journey to London by National Express Coach. Foolishly, I had not been as sensible as to arrange accommodation for my visit to the capital, but thought that I would surely be able to arrange something when I got there? Eventually, I arrived in the Capital and as I had not been to London previously, I had little idea as to which direction to head in my attempt to find the arena.

A few hours later, after much searching and inquiring, I found myself outside the venue. I had time to spare and got myself something to eat before making my way into the auditorium just as the support band was coming on stage. This was just incredible, what an atmosphere was I about to see Hawkwind after waiting so long?

The air was filled with the sweet smell of cannabis, but my adrenaline was flowing and I was on an artificial high of natural endorphins and euphoria. Eventually, Hawkwind took to the stage and the crowd erupted, the hairs on the back of my neck stood to attention as the band welcomed everyone to the Sundown. Hawkwind then exploded into their first number, 'Brainbox Pollution'.

I was mesmerised as they continued their set and played without a pause between songs. Behind the band, there was a giant screen onto, which animated images were projected representing each of the songs being delivered to the admiring audience. As they played, an astonishing light show lit up the whole front of the stage, making the performance even more dramatic.

What an experience, what a show, the gig was spectacular, much more than even I had expected, and in honesty, there aren't enough adjectives in my vocabulary to explain the brilliance of the show. I was speechless and impressed as never before. At the end of the performance, the crowd exploded with appreciation as the band left the stage, only to return minutes later to deliver an explosive encore, their final number being 'Silver Machine'.

That night was something else, something I cannot explain, something that will live with me for the rest of my life, something only a Hawkwind fan can appreciate. All too soon the show was over and reluctant to leave I resentfully made my way out of the arena and through the streets of Brixton still buzzing with excitement and delirium, I felt like I was floating through deep space and without the need for an artificial substance.

My desire to see more of the band was simply insatiable. As I walked through the streets of London, the people passing by probably thought I was crazy, smiling to myself one moment, then remembering the song list and singing away to myself the next. Who needed drugs when such a rush could be gained in this way?

Unknowingly, I was about to fall to earth with a heavy bump, as I encountered problems later that cold January night. During that fantastic Hawkwind concert, I had had the good fortune to meet countless like-minded people, several Scottish guys who, like me, had travelled down to the concert by coach, a journey they had made previously.

They were extremely friendly and had told me that as their coach, like mine, wasn't due to leave until the next morning they had planned to allow themselves to be locked into Euston Station so that they could sleep there. This idea didn't fill me with much inspiration, although I was tempted and in hindsight, I should have allowed my temptation to rule; instead, I decided to make my way back to Victoria Coach Station.

I had been told that, provided you had a valid ticket of travel, you could sleep on one of the overnight-parked buses. It was now well after midnight and a handful of coaches are parked indiscriminately in the now desolate station. I found the coach that a few others had already boarded and I climbed aboard and secured one of the many empty seats.

I had only been seated for around thirty minutes and there were probably only half a dozen other people on the bus with the same intent as I or so I thought. I felt fairly comfortable with my legs tucked up covered with my Afghan coat, that was until two adults and a young girl got onto the coach. I assumed that all three were together, but unfortunately, I could not have been more wrong.

The lady and her daughter sat two rows behind me and the man sat next to me despite all the other empty seats. I thought it odd but, in my naivety, I didn't question this, thinking that all three were together. When only a few moments passed, his hand brushed against my knee. In my continued naivety, I thought that this was a straightforward accident and I pushed away his arm.

Sadly, I was very wrong and immediately his hand took a firm grip on my left leg. Realising with alarm what was happening, I immediately jumped to my feet and forced my way past this pervert and headed off the bus. The man remained firmly implanted in his seat as I took one final backwards glance.

Now shaking and frightened, I walked briskly out of Victoria Coach Station and wondered what to do on this extremely bitter January night, a hard frost now covering the ground. Dressed only in jeans, a t-shirt and an Afghan coat, my hands felt numb from the brisk cold winter wind. Thankfully, I discovered the Salvation Army soup kitchen and made the best of what had been a disturbing event.

Fortunately, the incident did not detract from my enjoyment of finally seeing Hawkwind live and early the following day, I jumped on the bus to head back to South Shields, where I was eager to tell my friends of the brilliant performance I had at last witnessed. Having now experienced Hawkwind live, this was never going to be enough of this visually stunning and amazing psychedelic band.

Hawkwind offered something no other band could deliver; the unique blend of space rock, a spectacular light show and even an exotic dancer, the fantasy of many a young man. For me, travelling around the country to see Hawkwind would almost become a full-time career; in fact, I always had aspirations of joining the band as one of the road crew – would that be part of my fate?

Sadly, that was never to be. Perhaps if illness had not intervened then that dream might have come to fruition, who knows? Instead, I had to make do with seeing the band play at many venues around this great country of ours. It also allowed me to make friends with other like-minded individuals.

Back at home and acknowledging that the current Hawkwind tour was in full swing, I browsed the tour itinerary posted on my bedroom wall and I noticed they were to play Leeds University in mid-February. There was no reason why I couldn't make the relatively short trip to Leeds to see that performance too. Life was good; life could not get any better, but it could certainly get worse!

Returning from Leeds, I was feeling exhausted. I was now enjoying life more than ever and felt this fatigue was due to my travels. It was a Friday, downstairs in the Ship and Royal was not only the place where the local rockers met, but it was also the venue where a variety of drugs were exchanged for cash.

Equally, I will not try to justify or argue the case for drug-taking but, for me and the circle of friends I associated with, Cannabis was smoked on a regular occurrence. I only took LSD on a handful of occasions, probably only because of the as yet unknown intervention of illness. As a believer in fate, I would argue that things happen for a reason and, therefore, had it not been for the intervention of cancer, then illegal drugs may well have destroyed my life at a relatively young age.

Friends at work had similar tastes in rock music and subsequently invited me to join them at their local pub. Evenings at the Marsden Inn would become an important social event on most nights of the week; I now had a group of friends with whom I could readily identify. They enjoyed my kind of music and we would take in regular live bands at a variety of venues around the region.

Saturday night was a rock disco at the Commando in South Shields, an upstairs room in a dishevelled pub, threadbare carpets covered the floor and the sweet smell of hashish filled the air. Many rockers who attended the Commando were indeed into stronger drugs, such as Cocaine and even heroin.

Significantly, however, despite being an impressionable and immature teenager, I was consciously aware these were not for me and I can honestly say that I was never tempted to try these harder, potentially addictive substances. Despite being embraced into their fold for almost a year, I would, unfortunately, lose contact with my newfound fraternity but not by choice.

I had other friends, of course, but they had different priorities than I did and most importantly, they did not share my passion for rock music. Some of the guys I knew had some musical talent, significantly more than I did. They had decided to form a band and had invited me to be the roadie and arrange the sound system and quite naturally, I jumped at the chance, recognising this could be my first opportunity to begin a life of rock and roll.

They had named themselves 'Shelter' and after some months of impromptu rehearsals an agent arranged their first gig at a local workingman's club, this could be the first tentative step to rock stardom and I was part of it. Life was moving in a direction that gave me great pleasure; sadly, however, something was lurking just around the corner, which would soon put a stop to my current enjoyment and which would take my life in a different and unexpected direction.

The band felt as prepared as they could be and so we hastily crammed the musical equipment into the back of a beat-up Transit van, which had definitely seen better days and headed down the A19. Having no vehicle of our own, we managed to persuade its owner to transport us to this most important event, hopefully, the first of many gigs to come.

The show was at Shiney Row Club and on the night, everyone was on a high as we set up the stage and sound checked ready to be on stage at 8.00 p.m. Naturally, being their debut, the lads were nervous and subsequently felt the need for a few beers. Before we knew it, the master of ceremonies came on stage, stood to attention behind his microphone and said, 'Please give a massive welcome for Shelter.'

Rapturous applause came from the unsuspecting audience, who sat back in eager anticipation. The agent who had booked the gig had informed the band that this was a 'rock night', which, as it turned out, could not have been further from the truth. The lads marched onto the stage like proud gladiators being welcomed into the Roman Coliseum; they quickly armed themselves with the appropriate musical instruments and then blasted out the guitar riff introduction to 'Johnny 'B' Goode'.

The lead singer jumped around the stage like a contorted epileptic, writhing and twisting before the first words came from his youthful throat. At the end of this number, the singer was puffing and panting and I was doubtful whether he had the stamina for the rest of the show. Certainly, the audience were not impressed, it was clear from their muffled grunts and groans that they weren't expecting a 'rock night!' but something more like 'Darby and Joan.'

Still, in the good old show business fashion, the lads were keen to continue their distinguished performance. Sadly, the second number, a number by the Allman Brothers Band number proved just as unpopular as the opening number and the compere immediately ran onto the stage to put an end to the boy's performance and the noise they had proudly presented.

I cannot remember his exact words, but the message was abundantly clear. 'Get off!' Needless to say, the boy's embarrassment was sky-high and they refused to go back on stage to clear away the equipment; instead, that was left to me and the other roadie. It was an unnerving experience, clearing the stage to the ogling eyes of two hundred beer-swilling pensioners.

One of the lads, Ralph, was so embarrassed that instead of leaving the building, by the way we had entered, he decided to climb from the dressing room window and into the awaiting transit van. Meeting with Ralph some thirty years later, he would profess to still be mentally scarred from that experience.

On the way home we had a good laugh about the entire experience and looked forward to the next gig, although at that time I was unaware that that would be my first and last gig with the boys, but not by choice.

There were many escapades in the shipyards too and it was remarkable that ships got built. One chap called Plank; I'll let you decide why this was his name, let's just say, he was not the brightest bulb in the box. He would often fall asleep during an afternoon break and, on one occasion, we welded the steel caps of his boots to the deck of the ship and left him to awaken in surprise. Another character was Irish; he was an apprentice burner and was supposed to be burning something off the inside of the ship's shell.

Unfortunately, he burned through the wrong area of the shell, causing water to seep into where he was working. He was not popular when the foreman discovered his mistake and that's putting it mildly. I was seventeen and enjoying life fully. If this was what life was all about, having fun and following Hawkwind from tour to tour, then life was sweet.

My goal at that moment was to get backstage and meet the band during their next tour. That was going to be a difficult feat and it was, but for a reason, I did not expect. The band had recently released their new album 'Hall of the Mountain Grill' and one particular track was exceptional, packed with emotion and incorporating haunting keyboards.

It immediately became a favourite of mine; in fact, it remains a favourite to this day. It was called 'Wind of Change' and paradoxically, that's precisely what I was about to experience.

Hawkwind had already completed a successful tour of America earlier in the year and now they were on the road again in the United Kingdom. They were scheduled to perform in the North East on the 12 December and, this time, I would get to see them at Newcastle City Hall, as I would in the following years.

Sure enough, 12 December would be a fantastic gig, if anything; they were much improved from earlier in the year. Two days later, I travelled to Manchester to witness the band at the Palace and at that moment, life could not have been any better. Yes, life was cool, what more could a young man want from his existence?

Had I not needed the commitment of work to finance my following of Hawkwind, then I would have simply made sure that I attended each show in each city of each tour. In April of the following year, I decided to make the journey down to Dunstable to see Hawkwind before they started to tour America later that same year. On the 13 April 1975, in complete innocence of what lay ahead, I travelled to Dunstable and the Queensway Hall.

Sadly, after a long and exhausting journey, I felt the performance on this occasion was not the power-packed space rock that I was becoming accustomed to, it seemed a somewhat indifferent performance, but perhaps it was me? During the show I was unable to maintain a steady degree of concentration and my enthusiasm was waning, not for the band, far from it, it was more my physical well-being as my vigour seemed to be draining from my body.

I had absolutely no idea what was causing my fatigue, other than perhaps the long and tiring journey to Dunstable? Despite my weariness, I felt that my long trek south had not been in vain, I still had aspirations to join the band in some shape or form and understood that not every performance would be great, although the onset of my extreme tiredness still puzzled me; my exhaustion was overpowering and I was subdued by its superior force.

When I returned to work I was still exuberant from the gig. I was slowly but surely beginning to realise that this fatigue had been consuming me physically for many weeks. I had been feeling decidedly weak, even during my trip to Dunstable, I hadn't felt well and in hindsight, it was the euphoria of the gig and seeing Hawkwind live that had masked the overwhelming malaise.

I recalled that only weeks before my trip, I had been struggling to motivate myself to go out after work and on most nights, I'd just go straight home, eat with the family and then fall asleep in front of the fire. However, such was my enthusiasm to share my experiences of the concert that I did return to work following the Dunstable gig at the time and unknown to me, that would be my last day at work for some time.

It was becoming increasingly difficult to motivate myself. At times, I was struggling to breathe and it seemed that all I ever did was sleep. In addition, I had lost a significant amount of weight, but out of nothing besides ignorance, I had no concern about this, even though at that time I weighed just a little over seven stones.

Other symptoms included drenching night sweats, that were so profuse that the entire bedding had to be changed. I had an intractable cough, which would eventually; once I was admitted to the hospital, require Methadone to settle it.

In addition, I had also developed breasts, medically known as gynaecomastia, admittedly only small ones but again out of naivety I thought nothing of it. Furthermore, slowly but surely, my skin was taking on a yellow tinge called jaundice.

By this time, I had already made several visits to my family doctor, but he was about as much use as a chocolate fireguard, insisting that I was depressed and prescribed anti-depressants, Valium to be exact. I did not think I was depressed, quite the opposite in fact, but if the doctor said that's what it was, who was I to argue?

Following each meal and with increasing ferocity, I would vomit, while most of the time I simply felt nauseated, but why was this happening, is this what happens with depression? A constant lethargy accompanied each moment of every day and often I felt dizzy and disorientated. Strangely, I complained of having weak legs, a sort of tingling in my knees, yet my mobility was not affected; I could not begin to understand the bizarre changes that were happening to my young body.

I could not begin to describe the tiredness that enveloped my every movement, other than to say the exhaustion was overpowering. Even at rest I was completely exhausted and I accrued many sick days, but regardless, I did make every effort to get to work. The Shipyards were no different to any other industry; a minority of managers took their role so seriously that it became an all-consuming pastime.

They treated all others with complete disdain and contempt, which unfortunately gave the majority of manager's bad and undeserved reputations. Of course, for some of them, then the position would lend itself ideally to justifiable bullying and offensive behaviour.

Many others in those respected positions would play fair with the workforce, provided you completed your allocated work. For me, however, as an admittedly immature young man having turned eighteen only two months earlier, life remained a joke. And I took nothing seriously. Given my trivial approach to life, I would often find myself in conflict with a manager regarding some issue or other.

# Chapter 3
# Collusion is a Dirty Word

May 1975 was the month Led Zeppelin returned to England to play five sold-out shows at Earls Court in London, West Ham United won the FA Cup, beating Fulham two goals to nil and Vauxhall launched the Chevette, a small hatchback car. Only two months earlier, the Netherlands had won the Eurovision song contest with 'Ding a Dong', while the ageless, Shadows were admirable runners-up.

It was also the time when my life would change forever, marking the beginning of an experience that would not only manipulate my philosophy and develop my inner strength but would also make me realise something I'd never been aware of before; that my own mental and physical weaknesses were vulnerable. What I was about to experience would change my approach to every day for the remainder of my life.

This was my fate and my experience was to make such radical alterations to my mindset that, although I didn't know it at that time, I would eventually become eternally grateful for and positively reflective regarding the journey I was about to embark upon, a treacherous pathway of unknown proportions and a perilous journey of self-discovery.

There were periods of hope and optimism but, at the same time, there were moments when I experienced the darkest of nightmares unrivalled by any work of fiction. I was unaware that this forthcoming pathway would take me to the very edge of sanity, and threaten my existence.

Generally, I was happy, despite the unexplainable lethargy that dominated my every breath. The situation had now been going on for some weeks and the family doctor appeared to be none the wiser as to the origins of my current symptoms and was unconcerned. If he was not concerned, then surely I should not be either and I thought it would correct itself soon.

Yet despite that exhaustion, I managed to function - only a few weeks earlier I had dragged myself to the last game of the football season to see Newcastle United deliver a lack-lustre performance, and to be beaten by Birmingham City, finishing a disappointing fifteenth in Division one.

Despite my ongoing optimism of recovery from this inexplicable exhaustion, on an occasional night, I would be taunted by the thought that I would live with this unwanted fatigue forever. Despite my exhaustion, I still retained my interest in Hawkwind and they had yet another new album out called 'Warrior on the Edge of Time', which proved a real masterpiece. How ironic that very soon I would feel as if I was the one on the edge of time, perilously balanced between life and death.

With an effort that was becoming more and more difficult to muster, I was dragging myself out of bed each morning to try to cajole myself into work. One particular day, I was allocated a job in the cofferdams. These are the structures within the bowels of the ship, similar to the honeycomb structure of a beehive. The job would entail me physically dragging the welding cable down through the seemingly hundreds of manholes and into the double bottoms.

Naturally, there was no lighting down there and it was my responsibility to take a lamp with me so that the specific area could be illuminated. Trust me when I say, these cofferdams were well named; they were frightening places, black and deadly silent.

After dragging the cable down to the bowels of the ship, I was overcome with exhaustion and felt I couldn't breathe. I, therefore, decided to sit and have a short rest before starting the welding job expected of me. It was now around eleven in the morning and not surprisingly, as you might expect, such was my fatigue that I fell sound asleep, well, it could not harm to have a short nap, could it?

Some three hours later and I was awoken by one hell of a bang, my Manager had found me asleep. The siren had signalled lunch and everyone had been for their break and then duly returned to work. Everyone that was, except me and of course, this had not gone unnoticed. Jimmy was my manager and he had come looking to see what kind of progress had been made with the job, although as far as he was concerned I had gone absent without leave.

Imagine his anger when he made the difficult journey into the cofferdams and found me sleeping like a new born baby. Luckily for me, Jimmy wasn't a bad Manager, there were many much worse. What followed was the fiercest verbal rebuke, but I knew that I had got off lightly; many other managers would have sacked me there and then.

The following day to my verbal rollicking, I simply could not get out of bed as my weakness was getting steadily worse following another drenching night of sweats. No sooner did I stand up, the little energy I did have seemed to evaporate within seconds.

It made no sense and I was not strong enough to fight it, so I simply lay back down on the wet bedding. The night sweats were a specific symptom and caused such a degree of soaking that the bed looked as if someone had thrown a bucket of water over them.

Mum was working at the Scarlet Coat, a local and well-respected restaurant and knew I was too unwell to go to work and instead of hauling my weak frame down to the doctors in person, she insisted on a home visit. I agreed with her and later that morning the doctor arrived and immediately decided to have me admitted to the local hospital.

He suggested that my problem was not depression after all, but probably appendicitis, which would require an operation. This was quite a change from his original diagnosis and yet, he was still way off target with this new diagnosis. He then insisted on calling an ambulance and a blue light flashed me past the almost stationary traffic towards Ingham Infirmary.

The first investigation was a simple blood test, although this would be the first of many. Several hours later a blood transfusion was being arranged for me as it had been discovered that I was anaemic, a typical presentation of many cancers, although that word was not mentioned yet. Eventually, the doctor came along and placed a needle into the back of my hand without any explanation of the intended intervention, nor did he ask for my consent.

Soon afterwards, the nurse arrived at my bedside holding the bag of red fluid. That same night, some friends came in to visit me and attempted to make fun of the situation, but such was my weakness that I could not get motivated by their attempts at joviality and found little fun in their antics, no matter how well-intentioned. Still, it was nice that they had made the effort to come and see me. Well, for the now anyway!

Blood test followed blood test, followed by an x-ray, then the poking and prodding under my arms, squeezing my neck, then a hand on my stomach and a stethoscope on my chest and then on my back. Physical examination became a daily routine for a variety of doctors and, of course, more blood tests. Despite the almost constant investigations in those early days, I recall that they were long, lonely and painful days.

On occasions, I thought that my body was no longer mine; such was the intensity of the constant intervention, the prodding and poking and the ongoing barrage of the same questions made me feel as if they were designed to catch me out. Did they not believe what I had already told them? I vividly remember lying in a side room in the Ingham Infirmary with my radio playing and of course, regardless of which station I chose, there would be no Hawkwind.

Instead, I had to make do with commercial radio playing pop music; however, it served to break the monotony of those long, tiresome days in what for me felt like solitary confinement. As if it were yesterday, I vividly recall the record, 'Loving You' by Minnie Rippiton being aired. That song seemed to be on every station at ten-minute intervals and it drove me to despair.

Even today, if I hear it, there is a negative association with those dark and dismal days. What others might consider being a triviality, in that situation, feeling so desperately low, I felt that the disc jockey on whatever radio station I found; was playing this bloody record just to annoy me.

Despite the uncertainty of any diagnosis at that time, there was never any explanation of their investigations, no talk of what my illness might be. The days seemed never-ending and arduous, friendless, sad, perplexing and uncomfortable and quite often I wondered if I was just becoming paranoid.

Where the hell was fate taking me? The small fragment of optimism was replaced by despondency, as I lay trapped in this hospital bed, the marching sound of mystery footsteps passing by without a word being spoken. There was a cascade of voices down the corridor, too far away to hear what they were saying, but loud enough to understand that their laughter signified happiness.

Through the window of my internment, a large expanse of lush green lawn was occupied by a family of blackbirds, searching the soil for worms and beyond them, I could see the silent movement of traffic heading out of the town. All signs of life outside, that carried on as normal, whilst I felt all alone; my mind was unequivocally confused and frightened; unsure as to what was happening, unaware as to why I was feeling so terrible.

Between investigations and when time allowed, some of the nursing staff would make any excuse to drop into my cubicle and chat. As most of them were quite young, it was a welcome change to my own company and the mundane routine of examinations during those long, painful and generally unhappy days.

My despair was exacerbated by the fear of all the different investigations that I was enduring, what did they mean and what were they looking for? As I was given no answers or explanations, I couldn't help but wonder what they were hiding?

The night sweats continued nightly. Naturally, the nurses were aware that this was a symptom of my condition, but as a naive and immature eighteen-year-old, I was terrified that they would think that I had wet the bed due to incontinence. Such a silly thought, really, but it's remarkable what goes through an adolescent's mind at such a difficult time.

It seemed that there was an almost constant tirade of prodding and poking here, there and everywhere and I was perplexed at the nature of their search as explanations were not readily forthcoming. I suppose in many respects one could argue that I should have asked, but in all honesty, I was prepared to let them get on with it in the hope that once a conclusion had been reached I would be the first to know.

However, this would be a wrong assumption on my part. In addition, I was not a very confident young eighteen-year-old, therefore; I was content to let them get on with their search. There was the daily ritual of at least one doctor coming to see me with the very same questions that had been asked the day before.

Twice each week there would be an entourage of white coats dutifully following the consultant, all wanting to push me here and squeeze me there, listen to my chest and then looking quizzically at the Consultant, turning to him for words of wisdom. Meanwhile, one of the swellings in my neck had been surgically removed; the lump which was the size of a walnut and was excised under local anaesthetic then sent for microscopic examination.

The procedure, known as a biopsy, was a painless operation, but not all other procedures would prove so innocent or indeed painless. Later in the week, my bowels would be put through their paces in the search for a conclusion to my illness. The unpleasant and nauseating 'Barium Swallow' was a disgusting white concoction that tasted of, well, nothing I'd tasted before and it certainly was not savoury I can assure you.

The barium is impermeable to x-rays and, therefore, it is used to highlight abnormalities in either the stomach or the bowel after a series of x-rays have been taken. My bowels were taken to the next level of investigation when once again the radiology department would seek new ways to explore the inner depths of my colon.

I was wheeled into the x-ray room unprepared for this next exploration, as I had been given no prior explanation of what was to take place. As I lay on my side the radiographer told me of her intention, a plastic tube would be placed into my bottom and barium pumped in as if they were seeking to insulate my innards.

As I am sure you can imagine, it wasn't a very comfortable experience and I can certainly confirm that it was not enjoyable, but it didn't stop there. No sooner did the barium flow into my bowels like cavity wall insulation than the table, I was lying on started to twist and turn like a fairground ride.

This spinning and turning would enable a new series of films to see my bowel from different angles. Following this invasion of my dignity, I was only too pleased to get back to my solitary confinement for some peace.

The next day, I was taken across to the newly built diagnostic centre located at South Tyneside General Hospital for what was supposed to be one of the most important investigations, which would not only rule out one diagnosis but help to confirm another. I was taken into a small cubicle where I was met by a man with a fancy title, the Consultant Oncologist, who explained that the procedure I was about to undergo was a bone marrow investigation!

It didn't sound too bad or, was the Consultant just a good salesman? He went on to ask if I had any objections to the junior doctor doing the procedure. 'Of course not,' I replied, after all, a doctor was a doctor, what difference could it make? Not for the first time, my assumption was wrong. The junior doctor had no problem placing the local anaesthetic into the skin around my breastbone, where the biopsy was to be taken from.

However, he struggled to get any kind of leverage onto the biopsy needle he was using and which was supposed to extract a sample of the bone marrow from my delicate skeleton. Clearly, in hindsight, he lacked the necessary experience to undertake the technique with competence. His struggle was such that he climbed onto the investigation couch with me to force more pressure on the needle.

Yes, local anaesthetic had been used but, either there was insufficient of the dammed stuff in there or he had been a butcher in a previous life, alternatively, I was just a big softie. Seriously though, I was now struggling to tolerate the investigation and I think the Consultant realised this and he took over the procedure and secured the required sample in a few minutes.

Thank goodness that was over; I felt my chest was about to collapse like wet tissue paper. Once again, without explanation, I was wheeled out and transported back to the Ingham Infirmary for a much-needed rest and a large helping of painkillers. A couple of days later and my parents were taken to one side and told the news that all parents fear. My diagnosis was a malignancy, cancer.

It appeared to be a disease called Hodgkin lymphoma, stage IV and the outcome was far from favourable. Such was the extent of the disease that there was only a 50% chance of surviving and that depended upon how I responded to the treatment, failing to respond to the treatment would diminish the long-term chances of survival even further.

Lymphoid tissue malignancies are grouped into one of two diseases, those being Hodgkin lymphoma and all other lymphomas referred to as Non-Hodgkin lymphomas. These are uncommon cancers of the lymphatic system and are of unknown cause; Hodgkin lymphoma is most common among fifteen to thirty-year-olds, with a higher incidence among males.

Thomas Hodgkin first described the disease way back in 1832. Mam and dad were told by a Consultant that he would have liked to have seen me much earlier and he was rather bemused as to why I had been put on Valium and not referred to the hospital. In addition to the Consultant's bewilderment at the delay and the strange prescription of antidepressants by my family doctor, what would astound me was that, according to mam, the Consultant encouraged her and dad not to tell me of the diagnosis.

It seemed that was something they did not need a lot of encouragement to agree to. This was wrong on so many levels, but the decision was taken with the best of intentions and, of course, at the time, I had no idea of the collusion being acted out. I understand exactly why my mam and dad were happy to go along with this, as there is no worse sensation in the world than being told that your child has cancer and they would have wanted to protect me, but that doesn't mean I agree with the sentiment.

So, it turned out that I was not told of my diagnosis and therefore denied the opportunity to be involved in the decision-making process and to have at least some small degree of control as to what was going to happen to me. That's a basic right for any adult; surely it wasn't too much to ask for?

That decision by proxy still causes me great concern even today. It was my opinion that neither the Consultant nor my parents had heard of the veracity principle, which highlights the ethical obligation, to tell the truth or the underlying principle of patient collaboration, which regards the patient as being capable of making suggestions and of being involved in the decision-making process. I was that patient, but my voice had been silenced.

After the diagnosis, my dad visited his father to tell him of the devastating news and he responded by informing him that he had money in the bank and that if it was needed, it could be used to search out the best treatment that would afford me the best opportunity of getting well. However, dad did not take up this option and he and my mam placed their trust in the local hospital and its dedicated staff.

Having decided to exclude me from my diagnosis, the greatest concern now for my parents was trying to keep this information from me. However, their immediate concern was the fact that there was another Hodgkin lymphoma patient on the same ward as me and they did not want me anywhere near him, although unknown to them, it was too late.

I was undergoing all of these investigations to conclusively determine the cause of my symptoms, while Joe had already been diagnosed with Hodgkin lymphoma some five years earlier and was currently very poorly; he was terminally ill and sadly died during my stay on the ward. Only days before his death, I had sat with Joe and although I wasn't aware of either his diagnosis or his terminal state, even to my untrained eye I could see he was not a well man.

My mam in particular was especially concerned, in case, I discovered the cause of his illness and that I would not only be upset over his condition, but it could lead me to inadvertently finding out about my diagnosis, the diagnosis that was currently being hidden from me. This kind of problem occurs simply because of this type of collusion, although admittedly, they acted with the best of intentions, it was doomed to fail from the offset.

Furthermore, mam and dad had decided not to inform my younger sister, Allyson, about my diagnosis. Once again, the merits of this action can be debated, but, as Allyson was only thirteen years old, I could clearly understand their rationale for this move. It would be two years later before she realised that the condition was a cancer diagnosis.

Interestingly, Allyson would later confirm that she was pleased that she was not told, claiming that she would have struggled to come to terms with it. However, she could equally see things from my perspective and how frustrated I was at being declined the information that I was entitled to in the first instance.

Rather strangely, it seemed that all of a sudden, very few of my friends wanted to visit me in hospital and when I eventually got home, they were noticeable only by their absence. It transpired that mum had bumped into my best friend, Robbo, on the local bus and had told him that I had cancer. She also informed him that I did not know my diagnosis and her instructions were clear, under no circumstances should I be told!

It wasn't long before most of my friends were made aware of this stigmatising diagnosis and I later found out that the reason they didn't visit was their fear of the word cancer and not knowing what on earth they could talk to me about. Perhaps they thought the look on their faces would give the game away and they were worried about how I would react once I realised I had such the frightening disease of cancer.

I can understand why they were so fearful and I certainly do not hold any grudges towards them. Then again, perhaps it was their fear of my mam! One of the biggest dilemmas with a cancer diagnosis is the fact that many, sufferers, do not look unwell. It is a master of disguise, a hidden poison, a denizen from the unknown. And so it was that many of my friends would ultimately say that very thing.

You do not look as though you have cancer. But what does a cancer patient look like? It is not a respecter of creed, colour or social standing, everyone is at risk. Before starting any treatment, I was transferred to Newcastle General Hospital for some additional tests, which would determine specific issues relating to the lymphoma.

It was then that I was admitted to a specialist ward for cancer patients, yet when I arrived at the ward and even though some men had already lost their hair, due to my ignorance and naivety I did not realise that this ward was solely for cancer patients.

However, whilst in Newcastle General I overheard one of the doctors discussing my case with another and just by pure chance happened to hear the diagnosis of Hodgkin lymphoma. Now, this meant nothing whatsoever to me and I didn't give it a second thought, not knowing that this was a threat to my very existence. Coincidentally, the following day, I bought a newspaper and it seemed fate had then decided to take a hand and deliver an unexpected revelation.

One particular story in this tabloid would not only shock me, but it also caused me such heartache that my emotions erupted, tears being followed by anger and frustration. It brought a realisation that the life unfolding in front of me may well be shorter than I had hoped. The story in question had a headline; 'A Crossroads Star Tells His Sad Secret'.

The character and wheelchair-bound Sandy played by Richard Tonge in the soap opera *Crossroads* 'had been hiding a grim secret from millions of fans'; he was fighting his battle against Hodgkin lymphoma. Now, this interested me, as I suddenly realised that this was the same condition the doctors said I had.

Frighteningly, the article went on to reveal that Hodgkin lymphoma was cancer. I was completely taken aback, that couldn't be, right? My mind became numb and my emotions were everywhere, but where they should be. I paused for breath and had to read the article again, but sure enough, it was a cancerous condition. Why did no one tell me?

My mind raced, my head was spinning with confusion, a kaleidoscope of emotional turbulence. I experienced a whirlwind of changing feelings, nothing could have prepared me for such a shock, perhaps I had misheard or the doctors had been talking about someone else! Except, deep down inside, I knew they had been discussing me.

I now knew my diagnosis, but I certainly didn't know what lay ahead and the battle I was about to undertake. Undoubtedly, this was a roller coaster ride that I had never ridden before and I wanted to get off quickly, one moment I was up, the next I was on the bottom without any control over how to steer my life.

My breath shortened and my heart bumped so loudly that I'm sure the patient in the next bed would have heard it. I was fearful and panicking, unsure how to deal with these emotions. I plunged into elements of despair closely followed by an inexplicable euphoria and then, a tearful mood so low it scraped along the ground. So many other emotions and questions followed.

Anger! How dare my GP say I was depressed and what an insult that my so-called friends stayed away just at a time when I needed them most. Frustration! How on earth can I cope with a life-threatening illness? Suicidal! What the hell is the point of having treatment for what is a killer disease? Pissed off!

How dare my parents treat me like a child and keep this information from me. Guilty! Was this my fault, a result of my chosen lifestyle? Fearful! Would I be around to see the future? Doomed! As far as I knew, people didn't recover from cancer. Determined! I had so much to live for and boy did I want to live. Grateful! At least it was me, not my younger sister, Allyson. I experienced a myriad of emotions at the same time and there was nobody to help me deal with them; tearful and with genuine reason, I needed to focus. I searched my mind for motivation, for inspiration that could guide me and help my confused mind get through this nightmare.

In some respects, I had exactly that in the music of Hawkwind. However, there were times, many times when it was just impossible to control my emotions, times when my ability to focus was beyond my comprehension and times when I would need more than music. Emotions so intense, I struggled to grasp, or understand the gravity of my predicament.

Mam was completely flabbergasted when she came into the hospital later that day to find that I knew about the diagnosis, my diagnosis. She had come to visit with my dad and a couple of relatives. I wanted answers, but really didn't get any, but I felt this was not the time to argue. In addition and paradoxically, I could understand why they did what they did, even so, that still didn't make it right.

More importantly, I honestly didn't feel as if I had any fight in me or what little I had, I was going to need for the long, gruelling battle that lay ahead.

*'How did you think you were going to hide this cancer from me?'* I asked through gritted teeth.

Hurt and tearful, mam cried and I could see that dad was close to tears also, which led me to feel guilty for being so abrupt. They felt my pain during the months of illness and had tried to diminish it by protecting me from the diagnosis.

A diagnosis of cancer brings with it an alteration to every aspect, universally to your life. Your thoughts divert off at tangents during the most inopportune moments and serve as a constant reminder that cancer is a life-threatening disease. A convergence of negative and positive emotions would cause regular emissions of confusion and bewilderment.

Before discharge from ward 38, another blood transfusion was arranged as I was found to be anaemic once again due to the aggressive nature of the predatory cancer now stalking my body. On the day of discharge, I was started on a course of steroids, Prednisolone 10 mg three times daily and also a drug called Procarbazine, 50 mg three times daily.

The ultimate plan was chemotherapy, but with so many drugs being available to the clinician, the correct combination needed to be selected. The medical fraternity still needed additional information to select the correct choice of drugs to give me the greatest chance of beating this aggressive disease. The two drugs I had commenced would at least begin to exert some effect on my cancer.

Although not being aware of it yet, I would develop a crucially important relationship with ward 38 at Newcastle General Hospital, but that would be many years in the future. It would not only be instrumental in my illness, but it would also be significantly influential in my future years, fate being the governing factor.

Two days later and I awoke to find my body covered in an unexplained rash which caused me to want to scratch and peel the skin from my bones. Mam contacted the hospital and I was readmitted to the Ingham Infirmary for investigation, although I was not feeling terribly well, I could not say I felt any worse than the previous night before the rash appeared.

Despite this and an absence of other typical symptoms, the medical staff thought that this may well have been meningitis and I was, therefore, isolated and had the usual barrage of blood tests. It turned out not to be meningitis, it was a simple reaction to the Procarbazine and after stopping the drug it settled down after twenty-four hours of the appropriate treatment. Once again, I was on my way home.

# Chapter 4
# A Kaleidoscope of Emotion

The proposed treatment for this lymphoma was the dreaded chemotherapy, which was due to start the following Thursday as an outpatient at South Tyneside District General Hospital. Everyone has heard of chemotherapy treatment, hair loss, lethargy, vomiting and eventually, you die, that was my fear.

In the days leading up to Thursday's appointment, my mind was filled with thoughts of this terrible treatment that I was about to receive. Despite being admittedly immature, I wasn't completely stupid; I had seen television programmes about people with cancer and had seen the torture and torment they went through with this treatment and that terrified me.

On Thursday, I attended the outpatient department and almost immediately I was taken into a cubicle, not just any cubicle though, it was the same cubicle where the initially inept and torturous bone marrow persecution had been carried out only a couple of weeks earlier. The Consultant came in and passed the usual pleasantries and, I think in hindsight, his distraction therapy was perfect as I gave very little thought to the tray of large injections that lay only inches away from me.

He lifted the needle that he intended to place in my forearm ready for the delivery of the proposed drugs and before I knew it, he has access to my veins. It is quite strange the things our minds allow us to remember and forget, but it is with crystal clear clarity that I can still see that very first injection, almost in slow motion moving towards my arm, the rapid beat of my heart accompanied by its rising volume—a clear indication that my fear was higher than any time previously and unsure as to how my deteriorating body would react to this toxic poison being pumped into it.

As the chemotherapy drugs flowed uneventfully into my veins, rating a zero on the scale of excitement, my initial thought was that this chemotherapy was a bit of a breeze, not the terrible treatment I had imagined at all or was I being too optimistic? Irrespective, my main thought was, would it be able to stop this cancer? That was the million-dollar question and no one could answer that question, even though I never asked it.

I do believe that much of the fear and stigma relating to cancer treatments must be laid at the door of the media. How sad it is, when they could have an educative effect on the public, they all too often tend to sensationalise cancer and its necessary treatments. It's a great shame when someone comes along and is given a cancer diagnosis and told they need to have chemotherapy, then feel psychologically destroyed having previously read an article in a tabloid that portrayed the event so negatively.

I am not saying that cancer and its uncertain treatment is easy to get through or that it is not a serious issue; of course, it is. I just feel strongly that many, although not all, of the media, fail to report cancer facts accurately. All too often there is a sense of melodrama because it will sell newspapers or is good television.

That cannot be right if it is distorted to such a degree that it gives an incorrect perception to those undergoing or about to undertake treatment for a cancer diagnosis. The media have a responsibility to report matters precisely and without prejudice. The drug regimen I was going to receive was called 'MOPP', an acronym for the drugs to be administered.

The plan was to have six cycles of this treatment and each would be given at three weekly intervals, an important fact to remember! There had, in hindsight, been no formal or even informal consent for this treatment that was planned. Neither had there been any explanation of what I was to expect after the chemotherapy had been administered.

This is, in my view, is one of the most significant reasons why such stigma is attached to cancer treatments, a simple explanation of the potential side effects is vital and can allay so much fear from a patient's perspective. What's more, providing patient's with written information is a vital component of the empowerment process.

The drugs had been administered and the needle removed. That was my first chemotherapy treatment now behind me and I planned to make my way home. At the time, my grandfather lived just over the road from the hospital and he was aware of my diagnosis and had told my dad that if I felt up to it, I should call in after the inaugural treatment.

I didn't need a second asking, as my grandfather, William Slater Pattison, was a veteran of the First World War; he had been a prisoner of war, incarcerated in Döberitz, near Berlin. He had some incredible stories to tell and I loved hearing them. Therefore, after my first treatment I called in to see him for a short while, after all, my war had just started.

After a brief visit, I headed home, only ten minutes away by taxi. At home, mam had prepared one of her famous homemade mince pies. Of course, the steroids I was taking at the time ensured my appetite was voracious and when she asked '*How much of the pie do you want*?' I replied, '*All of it*'. The pie was devoured in no time.

Everything was going so well, I could not understand the negativity that went hand in hand with chemotherapy. This treatment had been pretty straightforward and not what I had expected or did my optimistic anticipation come too soon?

No more than twenty minutes later, my stomach began to gurgle and churn and then, to say that I was sick is perhaps the biggest understatement so far. I experienced projectile vomit from deep down within and I felt that my stomach had been turned inside out. In addition, it was not just a matter of being sick and emptying the contents of my stomach - as the retching continued for hours, which then stretched into many days.

During the night, the nausea was unbearable and the moment I got out of bed to visit the toilet, the very act of moving caused repetitive retching, which by this time yielded nothing but bile and brash which lasted for over a week. Unable to eat, fearing the sickness, my resolve was just about destroyed; I had never imagined anything like this and I could not believe that anyone could feel this way.

Disillusioned, feeling tortured and persecuted like never before my greatest fear was the fact that I wouldn't be unable to face more of this mental and physical torment, yet tearfully knew that I would have no choice and this was just the beginning. A week after my first chemotherapy and I was back in the hospital, but not because of persistent nausea and vomiting, I awoke one morning to find that I had the biggest lips that cosmetic surgery could buy.

It was yet another allergic reaction to one of the drugs I had taken and again, the Procarbazine was implicated. It seemed strange to me that the drug I had reacted to previously had been given to me again, but the Procarbazine was a vital ingredient of the treatment regimen and, therefore, they had decided to re-challenge my body with it.

This treatment was so unforgiving, was there anything it would not do to your body systems? Fortunately, after ant-histamine treatment, just a few days later, those rubber lips had disappeared. I was no longer controlling my body. It was being manipulated by the chemotherapy, leaving me like a drug-fuelled robot, an alien being with my actions controlled by the toxic drugs.

The treatment was repeated every twenty-one days, yet of those days, only ten were absent of the horrid side effects. Thankfully and without exception, my friends soon began to visit again. That is, once they knew that I was aware of my diagnosis and knew too that other visitors had not fallen into the vast chasm of silence and the fear of saying the wrong thing to their friend with the big 'C'.

My friends were very supportive and indeed protective. Later, in months to come when I would eventually feel strong enough to get out and socialise, the lads almost without exception would demonstrate big brother protection. If I was pushed the wrong way, even innocently, then there was always someone there to ensure that it was accidental and I was safe.

I very much appreciated this protection, feeling very fragile but also at times a little like royalty. Significantly, there were never any incidences of actual fights or other trouble and I knew that there was always a careful eye focused on me. It was almost three weeks from the delivery of my first treatment, but to my disgust and sadness; I awoke one morning to find clumps of hair on my pillow.

The cruelty of this chemotherapy knew no bounds; a tear rolled down my cheek to remind me of my mental instability. With anger in my heart, I decided to get my hair cut. It was pointless having long black locks that were certain to drop out as more and more of the dammed poison was pumped into my veins. I found this a particularly hard concept to accept.

My hair was an important part of my identity, my persona. Even my identity, as I saw it, was being eroded. My parents never commented on my hair, either as it started to fall out or when I got it cut short, as they just knew how important it had been to me. At a later time, I would destroy just about every photograph of myself during that difficult time.

Naturally, I was feeling quite low at that time and I required a sickness note for work, which meant a visit to my family doctor. I felt strongly that I would not see that imbecile that had the nerve and guile to talk about something he knew nothing about, the man who stated that I was depressed and then redirected his diagnosis to one of appendicitis. Instead, I asked to see the other doctor in the practice. However, I was just as taken aback when I went in to see her.

She looked me in the eyes having signed my sick note and said, 'Have they told you your diagnosis? Before I had a chance to reply, she blurted out, '*You have Leukaemia*'.

Mouth open aghast, you could have knocked me over with a feather. I snatched the sick note from her hand, told her that she was wrong and stormed out of her surgery without looking back. At home, I explained to my mam what had been said and she was so enraged that she rang the practice demanding to speak with the doctor.

Luckily for the doctor, she had gone out on a house call, which was probably just as well because mam would certainly not have held anything back in her reprimand of the doctor's insensitive behaviour. Mam did speak with the receptionist and told her exactly what she thought of the doctor's lack of communication skills, so I am sure it would have got back to the doctor. One of the most important lessons my sister and I learned early in life was that you do not answer my mother back.

Days before my next chemotherapy treatment was due again I began to feel physically sick, I knew exactly what I was about to experience, sickness and vomiting, twisted bowels and an inability to eat food for days, although it was not so much an inability to eat food, more of a fear of eating as it was obvious what the consequence would be.

Apart from that, well, it was a breeze, nothing to it! But if only that were true, if only this were a bad dream and I could awaken from my nightmare. I could never have imagined that this foreign substance deep within my veins could cause such devastating effects; effects I'd never even dreamed about in my worst nightmare, a storm of unforgiving proportions.

The day finally came when I was to attend the day unit at South Tyneside District Hospital for my next chemotherapy treatment. I got there in plenty of time and had my blood taken and made my way around to the yellow waiting area and, at first, I was saddened at what I saw—so many old folk, whom I assumed were there for the same reason as me.

Not saddened at the sight of the old people, but at the thought of these people who had worked all of their lives and enjoyed what life had to offer, only to be blighted by this terrible affliction that is cancer. Yet, here we all were without much control over this feared disease, irrespective of age, amalgamated by the same bond.

Such negative thoughts made me think of my mortality and whether I would be around for the next Hawkwind tour and if I was, would I be well enough to sit through a concert without feeling sick. In the background, a voice shouted my name and it was my turn to see the Consultant for my treatment.

I sluggishly dragged my feet into the consulting room to be faced by Dr Sheppard, who was a pleasant enough chap; it was just that I didn't feel very much like being pleasant, knowing what I was there for. He reminded me of Jerry Lewis in the starring role of the film 'The Nutty Professor', dressed in his long white coat, his glasses perched on the end of his nose as he peered over the top of them at me, a slight overbite and frowning as he stood alongside me as I lay on the couch, his feet clad in open-toed sandals.

Following a brief chat, he would twist his face up, just as the 'Nutty Professor' did in the film. Then following a physical examination, he told me that my blood is satisfactory, the lumps in my neck and under my arms have started to go down and that the next treatment would be going ahead as planned.

Then, although the words stick in the back of my throat, I bravely ask the question that I was dreading the answer to, '*Am I going to get better from this*?'

Now, I cannot remember his exact words; actually, I don't think I recall any of his words, only the interpretation and I think looking back his answer was what is commonly referred to as spin, also called deflection. What I do remember is that I was none the wiser following his response. But then perhaps I wanted to avoid knowing and I decided to allow fate to take its course, thinking that what I didn't know couldn't hurt me and therefore, I did not pursue it any further.

Before I knew it, the cold steel needle was in the back of my hand and ready for the delivery of the toxic drugs. Three of the drugs were given this way, the first an anti-sickness injection, although I was completely bewildered as to why it was called an anti-sickness drug because it was about as much use as my family doctor and we know how good he was.

The second was a large volume of fluid which was called Nitrogen Mustard and was responsible for nausea and vomiting. The third drug called Vincristine and had the weirdest taste and smell sensation as it was being administered, a foul unpleasant metallic taste and a bizarre irritation to my nasal passage.

There did not appear to be any of my body systems that were not being affected, attacked or destroyed by this treatment. I felt that I was being systematically and unceremoniously ravaged.

During subsequent injections, I would ask for a large glass of orange to sip very slowly while the Vincristine was being given and although it did not eliminate the taste, it did help. As I defencelessly watched the drugs seep into my veins, my heart raced, my emotions bubbled to the surface and I felt tearful.

I was anticipating the violent sickness that I knew lay in wait, fearing more unknowns and, of course, something I believe is typical of all cancer patients, the uncertainty of what lay ahead in my future, the ultimate question spinning around my head, did I have a future? After completing the chemotherapy for the second time, I headed home feeling unsure about how and, indeed, if I wanted to continue with this ruthless treatment.

At this particular moment, however, I felt that I had no other option than to continue, at least for the time being. That was something that would plague me on and off for many months, causing inner conflict and self-confrontation. I decided not to call into my grandfather's this time as I felt it would be better not to start feeling sick in his house, after all, he was in his late seventies and that would have been unfair.

Once at home, I decided to eat only a light snack as the large portion of mince pie had been the trigger following my first treatment, the doctor had changed the anti-sickness medication this time, so I was hopeful that I did not suffer as I did with my first treatment, fingers crossed. Sadly, within a couple of hours, I knew what was to follow, even though I'd only experienced it once previously, there was no mistaking that feeling.

Following the predatory attack of the chemotherapy on my body, my stomach was preparing to erupt like an active volcano, waiting spontaneously to spew its contents once again. Sure enough, there was a crescendo of nausea followed by the sickness and my stomach was soon aching as it had three weeks earlier. All I could do was retire to my bedroom, close the curtains and play some Hawkwind music.

Whilst it probably sounds silly to most people, it gave me a sense of escapism and I suppose most importantly, distraction as I lay on my bed, confined by a chemical straightjacket with no escape. Irrespective of your situation, I believe everyone needs inspiration and motivation, but Hawkwind was far more than simple inspiration at that time; they are, as many will testify, a way of life, to love them is to be part of them, to enjoy a romantic affair with creation, invention and space rock.

Weeks later, I was naturally pleased to read that the band planned to tour later in the year and this gave my deflated persona some much-needed inspiration. More importantly, as part of the tour, they were due to headline at the now-famous Reading rock festival. I intended to be part of that experience, to soak up the atmosphere, a free spirit destined to be part of the Hawkwind experience and the thought of this was a great driving force for me.

I was struggling to come to terms with this evil cancer and, at times, my mind was constantly buzzing, fearing the impending and indiscriminate attack of the chemotherapy. Of course, I knew there was no point in adding to my woes by worrying, but that was easier said than done, as I could quite simply not control the strange and fearsome thoughts lingering in the canyons of my mind.

At other times, I felt ashamed at the way I was feeling sorry for myself and there were times when I wanted to give myself a good kicking to try to pull myself together. I knew deep down, despite being an immature eighteen-year-old that I had to stay focused and positive. In addition, I felt I was being unfair to my very supportive family by being so negative.

I had unconsciously decided early on in my journey that I would not share my innermost secrets, my fears and my depressive thoughts with my family. They were indeed suffering the same as me and I wanted to avoid adding to their burden. Family life continued and seldom was there any discussion about cancer or treatments.

I would always undertake hospital visits alone, unaccompanied by choice and that was a huge mistake! Between treatments, I had family and friends visit on regular occasions but more often than not I simply could not be bothered by visitors, but I felt obligated to make trivial conversation.

Not only that, my friends, in particular, were always talking about their nights out, what they had been up to and, of course, the sticky scrapes they had got themselves into. I felt more depressed after their visits as I was becoming aware of what I was missing out on, the excitement and mischief of adolescence, including girlfriends.

At other times, this talk just fuelled my motivation to try to beat this horrendous illness. It was a lonely time when isolation played weird mind games with my psychological status. But importantly, I found this a time of personal reflection and self-assessment to take stock and to appreciate life itself. A time when I was thinking about things that I'd never considered previously.

To acknowledge that life is made up of simple but beautiful things which we often do not appreciate; the myriad of glistening stars floating effortlessly in the infinite darkness of endless space, only equalled in number by the grains of sand on the beach; the hypnotic sound of the waves massaging the unprotected shoreline without rest, watching the marshmallow clouds drifting across the skyline as a variety of birds soared on the invisible thermals beneath and the rhythmic echo of raindrops caressing the window as you lie in bed.

Louis Armstrong was exactly right when he said, *And I think to myself, what a wonderful world.*

After we are born, the only certain fact in life is that one day we will die; the only variance for us is when and how. Often, it is only after some life-changing experience that we consciously reflect on life generally and appreciate its significance, its sanctity, its beauty and of course, its uniqueness.

How many of us have ever taken time to sit and admire the everyday world, just simple things like the wind rustling through the creaking branches of an ancient oak tree? Then, of course, there is nothing more impressive than the first snow flurry of winter, taking a handful of virgin snow and feeling each of your fingers tingle with numbness.

What a fantastic world this is and yet we know so little about life itself. There is so much to admire and respect about life and its uniqueness but, sadly, there are so many things in life to fear, including illness, but ultimately, what is the meaning of life? No one has that answer and, perhaps, no one ever will. What I do know is that confronting your mortality has a strange way of raising many intriguing issues, allowing you to see life from a different perspective.

A cancer diagnosis also elicits the bereavement process, grief and feelings of loss are not just reserved for those individuals who have lost loved ones. Following a diagnosis of cancer, one goes through a multitude of recognised emotions; Denial, this can't be happening to me, it's a dream; Anger, why me, I've never done anything to deserve this; Bargaining, I will live my life respectably and go to church if only I'm well again; Depression, something I would become accustomed too; Acceptance, if this is my time then I have to deal with it.

Of course, many people go through these emotions in many different ways and not necessarily in this order and many of the emotions are revisited too. But at this particular juncture in my life, I felt as though I matured very quickly, appreciating that life indeed, is a beautiful thing.

At times it was easy to be positive and look forward to the future. However, at other times I felt weak for allowing seeds of doubt to invade my mind and promote negativity about my future. I was consciously aware of my body image and it wasn't very good, I knew the importance of gaining weight to improve my seven stone feeble frame.

Monitoring my weight every day became an obsession, yet the pounds proved extremely difficult to gain as I continued to feel fatigued and nauseated and since food lacked taste, the task of gaining weight would prove hard in the short term. It was a vicious circle and for that moment in time, a no-win situation.

Hope is so important; it is a skill that you must hone and cultivate—if you have hope, anything is possible. But, my lonely thoughts persecuted my optimism and removed my hope, thoughts so dark and negative they created my tears, invaded every recess of my mind and I struggled to battle those demons.

I thought of life as a whole host of small islands of happiness surrounded by a deep sea of shit. You get onto one island and enjoy the happiness it has to offer, but all too often the tide swamps the island and you once again are left in the sea of shit, until you can drag yourself onto the next island, this epitomised my life.

When the time came to go back to the hospital for further treatment my mind was twisted and full of fear and indignation and no matter how hard I tried I just could not escape the negative thoughts in the back of my mind. Entering the hospital my body felt like a lonely, trembling leaf on the branch of a huge tree waiting for the autumnal breeze to take control of it and whisk it away to who knows where?

Concerned and anxious about the impending treatment, I attended the blood room and had the requisite samples taken before heading round to the yellow waiting area that I was now familiar with. Waiting for the results only compounded the anxiety and fear, as they would dictate whether treatment would go ahead or not.

The nurse shouted my name and as it reverberated, bouncing menacingly off every wall, I reluctantly rose from my chair and trudged into the consulting room, struggling to hold back my delicate emotions.

'Your blood is all fine to continue the next treatment,' I'm told.

However, just before the chemotherapy is given there is the inconvenience of the physical examination and as I was laid on the examination couch I knew that I was close to tears. Anger and uncontrollable panic set in and even though it was still early days in my cancer journey, I knew that feeling, the anguish and the doubt in my resolve and I knew I was beginning to falter as the chemotherapy was brought into the room.

My frail body lay uncomfortably on the couch as the nurse provided me with a large glass of orange juice to take away that horrible metallic taste and the uncanny smell, created by the Vincristine as it was administered.

The Consultant smiled and said, 'Make a fist for me'.

With my fist clenched and my eyes closed he slipped a needle into the back of my hand then reached for the first of the drugs and in it went without resistance. Without warning, my mind anticipated and my stomach began to object, the brash welled up in my mouth and then I just knew I was going to vomit.

No matter how I tried to control it, I heaved into the receptacle held by the nurse, tears now rolling down my cheeks, not just due to embarrassment, but also sheer fear and concern at the impending side effects I knew were lurking just around the corner. Dr Sheppard had no option but to abandon the remaining treatment and I was admitted to the day ward awaiting a bed in one of the wards.

A cancer diagnosis is like a stormy sea, the scariest tempest imaginable and which batters your body (ship), subsequently, you have to learn to navigate through the storm if you want to survive. As I lay on the bed, I was conscious of the footsteps walking around outside, the occasional laughter of the nurse's discussing their recent escapades and yet although they were only a few feet away, I felt as if I was a million miles away from everyone, abandoned by society.

Unwanted and uninvited thoughts wandering through my mind—I knew there was no benefit submitting to the darkness that consumed my mind and steer me in a direction of self-destruction, but, I struggled to fight it.

Eventually, I was subsequently transferred to Newcastle General Hospital where I would remain until my treatment was completed and the anti-sickness medication could be reviewed. When I arrived at ward 38 at Newcastle General Hospital, I was greeted by a member of the nursing staff and shown to my bed.

Later a young doctor came along to prod and poke around and ask the requisite questions that had already been asked numerous times previously. Unable to do anything about it, this repetitive questioning frustrated me although I could not be bothered to argue. Before I started that obscene treatment again, I was started on a drip that had the highest dose of Metoclopramide, an anti-sickness drug, which could be given.

The idea was to control the sickness before it started; well, it was an encouraging thought if it worked, but such was my experience to date I could not help but think that it wasn't likely to. Of the specific chemotherapy drugs, Mustine was the one with the greatest ability to cause vomiting. Therefore, given my current sickness levels, it was decided that my regimen would be changed and the Mustine would be replaced by a drug called Cyclophosphamide.

I managed to sleep for the duration of this magic, anti-sickness drip and awoke to find a nurse and doctor standing at the bottom of my bed, waiting to administer the toxic chemotherapy. In all honesty, except for a few butterflies in the stomach, I did feel relatively relaxed, perhaps because I had only just awoken and didn't have much time to think about the impending treatment.

I asked for the orange drink before they started and they both looked at me with bewilderment, I'm sure they thought I was crazy. However, there was no way they were starting that treatment without that orange, of that I was certain and more importantly, it was neither of those two who had to endure the bizarre and filthy taste of the Vincristine.

After the treatment, I tried sleeping but to no avail and decided to walk along to the day room with my drip.

One of the guys, Tom, greeted me and asked what I was having, "*I think it's called COPP.*"

I replied, "*similar to me.*"

He retorted and we immediately began to compare notes and it turned out that he also had Hodgkin lymphoma. He was in his early thirties and was a policeman in Cumbria. He told me that his wife had left him recently as she couldn't cope with his cancer diagnosis and I thought that I had problems. Tom and I struck up a good friendship over the coming months.

I clearly remember his optimism at the treatment he was receiving and recall being rather envious of his eternal positivism despite experiencing the same side effects as myself. Later in the evening having attempted some food, my stomach began to gurgle, churn and then erupt as its entire contents were deposited into a large vomit bowl. So much for the anti-sickness drip!

The next plan then was to try a drug called Lorazepam, the mode of action of this medication would not only sedate me it also had an amnesic effect. Have you ever tried sleeping in a hospital? Don't get me wrong I'm not being ageist, but some of the old men could not half snore; if there were a category for snoring in the Olympic games, I could nominate a few of these guys and there would be a very good chance one of them would walk away with gold.

At first, it was quite funny, the musical chorus of midnight snoring but then it became annoying and frustrating as my sleep was not happening, unfortunately not a great deal can be done about the noise problem. There were private cubicles on the ward but these were reserved for the more poorly patients, especially those who were dying. That very situation occurred one night during my stay in ward 38.

The ward was busier than ever before and the nursing staff appeared to be running around without pause and spending an awful lot of time around the old man's bed directly opposite to me. The curtains were secretively drawn around his bed and the light switched on. The remainder of the ward was in relative darkness as one doctor followed another doctor behind those curtains and when one nurse went behind the curtains she was soon followed by another.

Then, the light was switched off and the doctors and nurses made their way from the curtains but, significantly, left the curtains closed. Some while later I was awoken by one of the nurse's closing my curtains, having just closed those adjacent to me. Five minutes afterwards and our curtains were drawn back and there before me was an empty bed, freshly made linen neatly folded and no sign of the little old man who had been the scene of such activity only an hour earlier.

Sadly, he had passed away, yet another victim of unforgiving and ruthless cancer. My eyes filled with tears when I realised what had happened and a silent acknowledgement that this cancer was quite capable of claiming me also.

Many a night in the hospital would be spent in the dayroom, often with the night staff and I do believe it is important to highlight that I had nothing but admiration and praise for these nurses. What they had to cope with was not the most pleasant job in the world but still, their dedication and uncomplaining approach impressed me immensely.

Interestingly, I had noticed that several patients on the ward were not having chemotherapy, they were having a different treatment for their cancer and it was called radiotherapy. It seemed to my inexperienced eye that this was a far easier treatment option than the chemotherapy that my body was struggling to accept. Why was that not given to me?

I thought I would make the appropriate investigations on this one and perhaps get the treatment changed, as that would be so much easier and then perhaps I could get back to work and also the forthcoming Hawkwind tour. So, my mind was made up, I want radiotherapy. But, how wrong could I be?

Another fellow patient was Steve. Steve had a different type of lymphoma from me, but he was still going through the dreaded chemotherapy and that made us kindred spirits. In addition, he was about my age and, therefore, we had much in common. Steve was about to finish his chemotherapy and start radiotherapy.

Unknown to me at the time, Steve had an aggressive advancing disease that required radiotherapy in addition to chemotherapy. This demonstrated that these lymphomas were not only unpredictable but also indiscriminate and predatory. The Consultant came around later that Friday morning and decided that he wanted to keep me in for observation and monitoring until Monday.

However, he did not mention my request for radiotherapy that I had earlier submitted via the nursing staff and as he left, I felt betrayed, let down, disappointed and dejected. The nurse in question told me that she had mentioned my request to Dr Sheppard but he dismissed it out of hand as a viable option. Surely, an explanation of his rationale might have been in the spirit of good communication.

I suppose if I have one criticism of the medical and nursing fraternity back then it was the poor communication. As patients, we were aware that the majority of doctors and nurses were not prepared to confront or even discuss the patient's questions and fears regarding cancer. Peer support at that time was invaluable and I believe it is equally important today.

Patients essentially need each other as support. Yes, of course, we couldn't do without the medical and nursing staff. However, doctors and nurses go off shift and can then forget about work until they are next on duty. Cancer patients simply cannot do that, seven days a week, twenty-four hours every day; as a cancer patient, you are on duty permanently with malignancy as your main accomplice.

Often I and others would be up most of the night in the hospital, concerned at the uncertainty of the future and comparing experiences regarding different investigations and treatments and that support was and remains an invaluable resource. What about when you are discharged, out of the hospital and back at home, then there becomes a sense of isolation as that mutual peer support is lost until your next admission.

Needless to say, family members are essential, they do everything they can and most often a whole lot more. However, they quite simply are not in the same situation as you and therefore, the mutual support patients offer each other is priceless. By Saturday morning I was feeling much better, something was having the desired effect.

Tom had suggested that we took a walk outside to get the morning paper from a corner shop rather than wait for them to appear on the ward. This we did and as we headed back to the hospital, Tom suggested that we stop and have a drink in the public house next to the hospital. This seemed like a reasonable idea to me and so we did exactly that.

The pub was empty and we sat with a pint of beer passing polite conversation but, as our glasses emptied, it seemed that both at the same time we turned and faced each other, our faces becoming ever more flushed with redness and we just knew something strange was happening. Therefore, we returned in haste back to the hospital and onto the ward only to be greeted by the Sister who took one look at us and smirked.

"*I know where you two have been*!" she exclaimed.

We felt like a couple of young schoolchildren having been scolded by the headmistress. The drug Procarbazine is an oral capsule and forms a significant part of the treatment as it is taken for seven days.

However, unknown to Tom and me, it interacts with many products, including alcohol which causes the facial flushing that we experienced and although there was no major problem other than this flushing and the fact that alcohol would have a greater effect than normal, we did feel like a pair of idiots. This, the third cycle of treatment was certainly not as bad as the first two.

Was this because I was kept in hospital or due to the change to the anti-sickness medication or the fact that I was having treatment at the same time as others and had some serious peer support? On Monday, I headed back home feeling much more positive than ever before. When I got home, mam was in the kitchen and when I wandered in there she just smiled at me and looked down at the floor and there in front of me was a delightful little puppy, a cross Labrador/German Sheppard and she was a real beauty.

Sheba, as she would be named would be my new companion, a distraction from the thought and worry of cancer and its impending treatment. Unknown to me, mam had made the long travel of approximately fifty miles by public transport, just to buy this puppy for me. The background nausea was still present and this would remain with me for days to follow, but Sheba was a good companion and a great distraction.

The future treatments had been planned as an inpatient at Newcastle and this pleased me greatly as it allowed me ongoing contact with Tom and the other patients in the same position as me, the mutual support that went hand in hand with that contact was essential, support that only another cancer patient could provide.

# Chapter 5
## Bury my Heart at Wounded Knee

Chemotherapy is a crude form of treatment in as much that it cannot distinguish between cancer cells and healthy cells and therefore both are destroyed. This is one of the reasons that cancer patients are so vulnerable to infections as their healthy cells, which help to fight infections, have been reduced, meaning opportunistic infections can be life-threatening.

It was during one of my periods of chemotherapy that I picked up an infection and a large boil developed on the left side of my cheek. As my white cell count was low, rather than receding with anti-biotics the boil was getting bigger and angrier and more painful.

Mam was a great believer in the good old fashioned remedies such as the bread poultice and this hot and painful concoction was applied onto the offending boil but despite this so-called natural intervention, it made little improvement and on my return to the hospital, the doctor decided that it needed to be lanced (cut with a surgical blade).

This was not a pleasant experience and even today there remains a small scar where the boil was; demonstrating just how unforgiving chemotherapy treatment can be. Despite my previous inability to cope with treatment, rather ironically, I now found myself desperate to get on with the chemotherapy. My mental anguish aside, the assault and battery on my body; I recognised that the sooner I could get the treatment behind me, the sooner I would be able to move my life forward.

Unfortunately, on this occasion due to the persistence of the unsightly boil, I had to wait longer for the privilege of my next chemical torture. It was felt that because of the infection and the low white cell count, my treatment should be delayed for a further week. Whilst this decision made complete sense, this delay would also serve to prolong my usual pre-treatment anxiety and extend my mental persecution.

Living with cancer delivers many challenges almost every day and these challenges can often be unexpected. This huge boil on the side of my face was certainly unexpected and it caused me a great deal of distress, pain and psychological despair. The simple fact is that you do not earn respect from cancer as a disease; the truth is that it simply fails to respect you as an individual. It is the ultimate of challenges both physically and mentally.

My mood was once again at a particularly low ebb, my mind was obsessed and confused by the fact that I required more chemotherapy but uneasy that I had to wait for it. Soon, I would make my own treatment decision but not necessarily the right one. My life was being acted out in a maze, at every turn, an obstacle held back what little optimism I had and I questioned whether I had the strength to negotiate more obstacles.

But, only days later my negative mood changed as I was taken by surprise when I opened the front door to see the postman holding a large package addressed to me, Mr John Pattison Junior. I signed for the parcel and rushed inside to find that the parcel was sent from Aunty Mary and Uncle Jerry in North Carolina, they had sent me some authentic Indian wear, including a couple of headbands, neck beads, books, a waistcoat and a special wallet.

On each piece, there was a ticket demonstrating that this was indeed authentic, hand made by the Cherokee residents of Oconaluftee Village in the Great Smokey Mountains of North Carolina. Mam had been writing to her sister in America to keep her informed of my condition and treatment; at the same time, she had quite innocently mentioned my interest in Native American culture.

My mam's youngest sister Mary had married an American GI after the war and subsequently immigrated to America. Needless to say, I had plenty of time on my hands at present and reading would prove a simple way to pass the time; I opened the cover of *Bury my heart at Wounded Knee* by Dee Brown.

It gave a fascinating insight into the many facets of the native cultures but also told of the exploitation and persecution of the Native Americans and, once started, I found it difficult to put it down. I had only read a few chapters and felt that one day I must visit these proud yet undermined people.

At that juncture in time, I did not realise the impact this book would have on my life and what 'Wounded Knee' would mean to me in years to come. The inspiration I gleaned from those pages would prove motivational above and beyond Hawkwind. How exactly those brave, proud and yet exploited people would unknowingly influence my life was at this point, beyond my comprehension.

I wrote many letters to Aunty Mary and many of these included my appreciation of the Indian culture but, more importantly, my desire to visit America and significantly the indigenous people who had been so wronged by history. Perhaps one day that would be possible but, at this moment, I could not for one second imagine that the impact of this book and particularly the struggles of the Lakota people, part of the great Sioux Empire, would have such a bearing on what lay ahead.

Towards the end of July and just before the chemotherapy was due again, Hawkwind appeared at the Mayfair in Newcastle and I knew that I had to be there. Having finished *Bury my heart at Wounded Knee* I had a newfound focus and despite my ongoing malaise, I dragged myself to the show despite feeling completely washed out and drained of enthusiasm.

It wasn't until I arrived at the Mayfair that I realised I would struggle to stay for the duration of the show and all for good reason. Thanks to my ever-present companions, the dominant force of cancer fatigue and the ever-present feeling of nausea, I tearfully made my way out of the hall and headed home.

My resentment of this disease was growing stronger and stronger as the weariness continued to impact my determination to try to enjoy what pleasures I could.

Worse was to follow, as much to my disgust a chest infection followed close on the heels of the boil that had unceremoniously scarred my face. This infection forced me into hospital during August, which meant that I had to abandon my plans to travel to Reading to attend a rock festival, which was being headlined by Hawkwind.

My lonely persecution was intolerable. I felt isolated by a hidden disease and attacked by its very consequences, all my motivation was stolen.

To distract me from the disappointment of missing the Reading festival I decided to read more about the Lakota Sioux; they were, after all my new driving force, my absent guides, my inspiration to cope with an invisible illness and most of all I felt they could indirectly support my mental instability.

A few days after my discharge from South Shields hospital, the chest infection was now behind me. I made my way up to Newcastle for the fourth cycle of delayed chemotherapy; hoping that some of the guys that I had met on my last admission would also be there. Indeed they were and Tom and I met in the day room.

I was still bemused by the fact that some of the patients at Newcastle were having radiotherapy treatment and I was confused as to why it had not been offered to me. No one had taken the time to explain why I had not been considered for this treatment. Of course, there was a perfectly logical explanation which I would learn about later.

With me on this admission was Hawkwind, they had recently brought out a new album called *Warrior on the Edge of Time*, truly one of their great works and I had it on an audiocassette so that I could play it on the portable cassette player I had taken to hospital with me.

The first track, Assault and Battery, quickly became one of the many all-time favourites of mine and still to this day it will be played by the band during their tours. It had, I thought, a most appropriate first verse. *Lives of great men all remind us; we may make our lives sublime and departing leaves behind us, footprints in the sands of time.*

Being in the situation that I was, facing an uncertain future, with so many variables racing through my mind, I felt this could have been written for me. Don't misunderstand, I am not for one second saying that I am a great man, far from it, more the fact that it seemed I was leaving my footprints and nothing else in the sands of time, nothing else to show for my short time on earth.

Once this fourth cycle of chemotherapy was complete, I headed back to South Shields to await the arrival of my expected companions, sickness, lethargy, anorexia and isolation and the inevitable psychological doubt.

In September 1975 I managed to see my team, Newcastle United beat Aston Villa three goals to nil, which gave me a huge lift. However, later that month, I made perhaps one of the most foolish decisions of my young life to that date. I was starting to feel quite well, the lumps and bumps of lymphoma had vanished some weeks earlier and therefore in my humble, yet ignorant opinion, I thought that the 4 cycles of chemotherapy treatment had been sufficient and there was no need to continue with this chemotherapy, which was interfering with my life so drastically.

I decided enough was enough, even though Dr Sheppard had planned a further 2 cycles of treatment. I knew my body better than anyone or did I? So, after only four cycles of chemotherapy, I took the monumental decision to stop treatment without consulting the Consultant or any of his team.

Having examined my body and found no lumps, I gave myself a clean bill of health and therefore, to my naïve and silly mind, the chemotherapy had been successful and I had now finished the treatment that had caused untold upheaval in my young and as yet inexperienced life. It had robbed me of so many pleasures in life; altered my perceptions, both good and bad, made me bitter and mentally confused and placed me emotionally on a precipice.

So as the disease had controlled me for so long, I felt that it was long overdue that I took some control back. I foolishly failed to attend my next hospital appointment and even when a reminder came through the post a few days later, I ignored it. I felt that I had been living my life around cancer and that, in my view, wasn't right and in ignorance, I thought I would put the cancer experience behind me and with immediate effect! It was as easy as that, or so I thought.

Ten days later, early one evening, I was sitting at home watching television with my family, still trying to get my head around the notion that I had finished treatment and trying to be optimistic that my cancer would never return when I heard a loud knock on the front door. To my surprise and amazement, standing there was my family doctor, larger than life, his twenty stone frame obscuring the natural light.

He immediately went into a rambling narration regarding the importance of starting the treatment again because if I didn't, I would be organising my funeral. Not only was he, in my opinion, an incompetent doctor, he was also inept in his communication skills. What a bloody cheek coming to my front door and talking to me about funerals, but not just any funeral, my funeral.

In hindsight he did, of course, have my best interest at heart and, I suppose, although I didn't see it at the time, I was blinkered by his previous inaccurate management of my illness. Not wanting to hear the truth I told him to go away with perhaps one or two expletives!

Naturally, my parents wanted to know what the raised voices were all about and I remember feeling very bad and so deceitful when mam found out that essentially I had stopped the treatment of my own volition. As the tears rolled down her cheeks, my guilt surpassed stupidity, and tears of despondency filled my eyes.

I had let down not just my family, but also myself. I had failed to give myself the best opportunity of beating once and for all the lymphoma. Embarrassed as never before, I did the only thing I could and that was to escape to the secluded confines of my bedroom.

Mentally I tried to reflect on how the Lakota Sioux would cope with a situation like this but to no avail. Of all the chronicles of their plight and culture I had read, there was no description of managing a malignant disease.

I retired early to bed that night in September and felt at perhaps my lowest ebb since discovering my diagnosis, upset that the doctor had been so brutally explicit regarding my future and bewildered as to what course of action I should take now. During that endless night, I felt dismally lonely and confused like never before but also very tearful and without a friend in the world to advise me on the correct course of action.

I was annoyed by the attempts of others to stifle my exposure to the truth and had wanted control of my own destiny or at the very least some say in it. But now that I had control, I found it more than difficult to make what potentially could be life or death decisions. I felt this was a no-win situation. I consciously did not discuss my deep and innermost emotions with my parents simply because I knew the hurt it would cause as they too would share my anguish.

I was not convinced that I could honestly tolerate the onslaught of those drugs again and the inevitable consequences they brought with them and if I explained this to my parents they would be destroyed. With so much on my mind, I had very little sleep that night, but I think that I probably matured overnight as I hesitantly decided the following morning that my future could only be guaranteed if I completed the despicable chemotherapy.

I reasoned that if the experts were recommending this barbaric treatment then it must be necessary, they wouldn't put anyone through that just for the sake of it. I returned reluctantly to the Hospital on Thursday for my fifth course of those destructive drugs; acknowledging that once again, I would be living my life around cancer and I would no longer be in control.

To my surprise, the medical staff insisted that I have my scheduled treatment at the Diagnostic Centre at South Tyneside as an outpatient, rather than as an inpatient at Newcastle. I did wonder if the medical staff were now making an example of me because I had foolishly decided that four treatments were sufficient, but perhaps I was being somewhat paranoid.

At times it felt as if everything was conspiring against me and nothing appeared to go the way the medical team had expected, I couldn't understand how a treatment aimed at ridding your body of cancer would also damage everything in its path, my mind included! Sadly, the fear and anxiety about the expected side effects led me to feel nauseated even before I entered the premises, a feeling I knew all too well.

I can clearly remember feeling the sharp prick of the needle breach my skin and almost immediately, the cold toxic substance being pushed along the syringe and into my fragile veins. Emotionally, I was wrecked, my mind was just buzzing with the fear and knowledge of what the consequence of this chemotherapy would bring and I just could not face any more of this.

Once again, as had happened some months earlier the Consultant stopped the treatment with little of the intended drugs delivered. It was not just his compassion and sincerity; it was also the empathy of the nursing sister that made me feel even more upset and tearful. My body trembled, my head was spinning and I wept uncontrollably.

Only weeks earlier (August 1975), the Americans had launched the first of the Viking space rockets to Mars, where they would discover massive dry river beds – proof that the red planet had once hosted life. Such amazing science and technology; yet, medical science could not find a treatment that would eliminate from my body an unwanted host, a cancer that was freely roaming around inside me.

I was again transferred to Newcastle General Hospital and to the welcome embrace of ward 38 where a regimen of intravenous fluids and a similar cocktail of drugs that had worked quite well on my previous admission were being prepared. The chemotherapy treatment would not be given until the following day as it was now early evening.

I was kept in hospital for a couple of days following the chemotherapy and I deliberately did not come out of the cubicle for fear of meeting anyone I had previously hoped I would see. My unbalanced mental state was not ready for peer support and their reciprocal empathy, yet ironically, I missed that support.

Dr Sheppard came in to see me on Monday morning and told me I would be going home and that because of my inability to tolerate the cytotoxic chemotherapy, this fifth course would be my last, but—then came a massive but!

Sitting on the side of my bed Dr Sheppard told me that there was still evidence of lymphoma and it was very unlikely that the amount of chemotherapy that I had already received would be sufficient to control this highly aggressive cancer.

He looked straight into my eyes and said with conviction, *"There is less chance of getting rid of this cancer than previously thought, but as you have relapsed we must try."*

Therefore, he had decided on an alternative treatment, one that was gentler but would complement what had already been given. Despite this unwelcome prognosis I admired, at last, his honesty and openness and asked for some detail on what this alternative treatment was.

The new regimen would include some oral chemotherapy tablets called Cyclophosphamide taken for fourteen days. In addition, I would be required to take more steroids. But most importantly, another component would be a drug called Bleomycin, which was administered as an injection into the muscle of my bottom.

The plan was to have the injections twice each week for two weeks. What did I have to lose, it didn't sound too harsh and what's more, the Consultant had said that if I felt up to it, then I could return to work and have the on-site doctor administer the injections. To my frustration, the doctor at Readhead's Shipyard decided he wanted nothing to do with this chemotherapy and it was therefore left to my family doctor to give the injections—yes him!

In fairness, he did not appear to hold any grudges following our verbal confrontation a few weeks earlier and the treatment went uneventfully. The treatment wasn't too bad in comparison to what I had previously been given and it did allow me to get back to work, which was important to me as it would give me some normality and social interaction.

Despite being happy at work I found it very taxing and at the end of my working day, I simply had no energy for anything else other than sleep. The intramuscular injections were bloody painful and meant you couldn't sit for about an hour afterwards. Fortunately, this treatment only lasted for two weeks, after which I would then have a four-week break before commencing the next cycle.

Thankfully, after two months of this most unusual of treatments and after a physical examination, no lymph nodes could be detected and my blood count was normal. Dr Sheppard felt that I was in remission.

*"Was I cured?"* I tentatively asked.

His reply resonated throughout my head, *"Too early to say that I'm afraid."*

On my way home, his words swam in different directions around my mind. So, from my diagnosis in May, I was now coming to the end of a journey that began with the mishandling of my symptoms. I underwent many unpleasant investigations, experienced the devastating psychological effects of the unknown and felt betrayed and undermined by the attempts to keep my diagnosis from me.

The trials and tribulations of dealing with chemotherapy led to many mixed emotions; the optimism of recovery and then the depressive decline of realising that your very existence was always under threat. All of this culminated in my foolish decision to end my treatment in September. At last, now the treatment was finished, perhaps I could now put this whole chapter of my life behind me.

It was such a relief yet I felt somewhat isolated and vulnerable, gone was the safety net of the hospital. Although I would be back and forward for check-ups it would not be the intensive contact I'd been used to. I would also miss the comradery and support of Tom and the other patients whom I had met at Newcastle General Hospital and the welcome embrace of ward 38.

I felt that it was most important to get back to work, purely and simply to normalise my life, but to prove that the cancer was not going to dictate what I could and couldn't do in my life. On my return to Readhead's shipyard, I was asked to make an appointment with one of the training officers.

In his office, I was told that the management had decided that because of my serious condition then it wasn't practical for me to return to welding and I was allocated to the plating shed. This job was cleaner and also presented less toxic fumes.

My time in the shipyards was a pleasant one; the industry was full of some weird and wonderful characters. People such as Mickey F****** Broon, named because between every other word he used the 'F' word. He called me F****** shite hawk, his reason? 'He likes Hawkwind and he's full of F****** shite.'

I have no idea where he got his rationale from but he was a harmless guy. Jimmy the carthorse, my previous manager (the one who caught me asleep in the cofferdams) came up to me to ask how I was.

I think he felt bad about the verbal rollicking he had given me that day and said, "*You should have said you were poorly.*"

The truth was of course I did not realise how poorly I was and I felt quite sorry for Jimmy that day. Word had quickly spread throughout this small shipyard of my diagnosis and many of the older guys in the shipyards made an effort to come and speak with me that afternoon and that was important to me, even those men who hardly knew me suddenly adopted me as a friend.

The management at Readhead's shipyard was very supportive of my situation. If I wanted or needed time off work, then I only had to say the word. It was a good time, a time when life appeared to be getting back to normal or so I thought. As always in the back of my mind was the inevitable fear of cancer and the worry about how long I would be well.

Soon, very soon, I would have that answer. In the interim, for the sake of my mental health, I had to put those dreaded thoughts to the back of my mind and get on with life. Fishing would also prove to be an escape mechanism. Neil, also from the shipyards was a good friend and we'd spend many a night sitting on the edge of the rocks at Marsden fishing.

More importantly, when I'd go to his house, his wife, Jean would be there. Jean was a staff nurse and I had developed a huge admiration for the work that they did and I felt this was something I would like to do. At that time I had no qualifications, nor was I ready to leave a relatively well-paid job in the shipyard for a career in nursing, but talk of nursing excited and interested me and I imagined how much better it would be to have a fulfilling and rewarding career, rather than the mundane life in a shipyard.

Fishing expeditions with Neil would become regular occurrences; I clearly remember one night sitting on the rock edges peering into the black wilderness way out to sea and seeing a shooting star diving towards the earth. I'm sure there is no need to explain here what I wished for that night.

Between treatments, my friend Robbo and I would spend many nights at the City Hall in Newcastle seeing a whole host of different bands; it helped marginalise the deviation from normality and gave me a sense of acceptance, doing the things that normal adolescents do. By Christmas 1975 I felt better than I had for some time and I was getting out and about with some of the guys.

I knew their eagle eyes were constantly focussed on me and ready to protect me should the need arise; although fortunately, it was never necessary. More and more people would come up to me and ask how I was, even those that I didn't know too well and I appreciated this, a recognition on my behalf that people were true, well-intentioned and that the world wasn't such a bad place after all.

It was around this juncture in time that I realised what I'd missed over the past couple of years and I now enjoyed the social scene and felt quite optimistic. Unfortunately, my optimism was short-lived as mid-way through April 1976 I began to feel unwell. Only a few months after finishing treatment the tell-tale signs began to appear, lumps under the arms could indicate only one thing, the cancer was back again!

I had no other option but to get in touch with the hospital and bring forward my appointment. The sweats had once again started to pay me nightly visits and I was experiencing specific chest pains. The drugs, Bleomycin and Cyclophosphamide had failed to halt the determined advancement of this obstinate cancer. What would their approach be now? Would they have another approach?

Perhaps as a believer in fate, then I had to accept that my existence was not intended to be a long one and that eventually, this cancer would ultimately terminate my life. At the hospital, the obligatory blood test and physical examination confirmed that the lymphoma was once again becoming active and that further treatment would be required.

At least, I thought to myself, they were not giving up, even though I had an inherent fear of the treatment they proposed. I was told that there is a swollen gland in the left axilla and at least a couple in the groin. This represented a second relapse and as if they hadn't learned anything about communication the first time around, my mam and dad were taken to one side and told that it will now prove more difficult to control what is an aggressive lymphoma and also means that the original chances of a 50% survival rate are significantly reduced.

The evidence concerning the different drugs used by an Oncologist means that the first drugs chosen to treat cancer have the best chance of getting rid of the disease once and for all and my parents had initially been told that my chances of survival were approximately fifty per cent.

Lymphoma remained a killer and mam and dad were also told that this percentage would naturally diminish if I did not respond to the selected drug cocktail; this failure to respond is called a relapse or disease progression and I now had progressive disease.

During our discussions many years later mam confided that it would not be uncommon for her to cry uncontrollably and without warning such was her and my father's worry about my condition and, of course, the fear of losing their only son. Their helplessness at not being able to assist me to rid my body of the demon inside and its controlling effects was difficult for them to accept.

It was now that I expressed abhorrence at being confronted by more chemotherapy and I did not want this. To this end, I told the registrar who had informed me that the disease was once again progressing. I told him, that I could not guarantee that I would be strong enough to complete further treatment.

However, when he said that I would be going to Newcastle for treatment. To me, that meant only one thing, I was going to get radiotherapy, even though he never actually came out and said that. It was my way of coping, my twisted mind making the wrong interpretation of what he had said.

I had seen the other patients tolerate this radiotherapy treatment when I was at Newcastle and it appeared to be absent of side effects, so I agreed to attend ward 38 again the following day. Amazingly, at times we hear what we want to hear and to the exclusion of everything else. What's more surprising is the fact that we believe it too. This was one of those very examples.

On the ward, I found that things were no different than I remembered the same nurses were there but, unfortunately, there were no familiar faces among the other patients. The junior doctor on duty asked me the repetitive questions that I knew so well and then he proceeded to tell me that the chemotherapy would start later in the afternoon.

"*Hang on there!*" I said. "*I am not here for chemotherapy, I am having radiotherapy.*"

The young doctor looked bewildered, checked the medical notes and being somewhat confused trotted off to the office to clarify exactly what treatment would be given.

Almost immediately along came Syd, one of the staff nurses that by now, I knew very well. Syd tried to explain that chemotherapy had been planned for me and because my cancer was quite widespread throughout the body, then radiotherapy wasn't an option. At that point I became upset, I felt betrayed and let down, if that was all that was on offer then thanks but no thanks I was adamant I was not having more brutal chemotherapy.

I simply did not feel I could cope with all the physical and mental torture that accompanied that treatment, particularly as it offered no guarantee of a cure. I can recall quite clearly that Syd was taken aback by my response, but he then carried on telling me that this was my only option. But my mind was made up; I would not, could not accept more of this gruelling chemotherapy.

Syd sat at the bedside and spoke slowly and concisely, purposely and carefully choosing his words, delivering each sentence with genuine empathy, "*If you don't have the treatment you may not survive this cancer.*"

His blunt, but honest and accurate words echoed around my head. In the first instance, I felt anger towards Syd, thinking, that it was easy for him to sit there and say that, as it was not him stuck with this bloody cancer racing around his body and facing further chemical torment. Almost immediately I felt guilty for having those thoughts, he was only trying to help and it certainly could not have been easy to sit beside me, not knowing how I would respond.

At this point, I made perhaps the most important decision of my life. '*I am not having further chemotherapy and, if I have to die, then that's it.*' My decision was final, yet strangely, I did not find this decision difficult to make; on the contrary, I felt a huge burden lifted from my shoulders. Surprisingly, even to me, I remained very calm, but I do remember feeling very sad for my family.

It is difficult trying to convey this concept to anyone because people may say that you would cling to every opportunity and grasp any chance you have for life and yes, of course, some people would do that. However, the emotional turmoil, debilitating nausea, the gut-wrenching vomiting and the psychological confusion was beyond comprehension, the depressive isolation intolerable.

Anticipating how you're going to feel before it's even started was something I felt was not an option I was prepared to accept. Syd, however, not to be beaten, asked if we could discuss things in a more private setting and although I was adamant that I was not having chemotherapy I agreed to his request.

He did not try and directly persuade me to have more chemotherapy, instead he spoke of how he could not even begin to imagine what the treatment was like and I respected his honest approach. He also spoke of my family and the effect my decision would have on them. Eventually, after almost an hour, Syd, in some psychological process convinced me that chemotherapy was the route to take and so I very reluctantly agreed to further treatment.

I'm unsure if Syd realised exactly the monumental change of heart he had instigated that day, but one thing is for certain, he inspired me to continue and I do not believe many others could have done that. Syd would leave nursing and take up a role in social work and I would never see him again.

Curiously, I often wonder what might have been if he had not been on duty that day, I do not believe that many other nurses or indeed doctors back then would have talked so openly and honestly about death as Syd did with me. If you happen to read this Syd, I owe you so much and thank you.

I believe that in many regards, some nurses and indeed some doctors working in the demanding field of cancer care become therapeutic friends to patients, but it's difficult to see sometimes where this relationship starts, where it ends or does it ever end? What is certain is the fact that without these therapeutic friends, cancer patients would be lost.

Subsequently, for me, it was chemotherapy time again. The dosages would be reduced from what had previously been given due to my inability to cope with the wrath of this infernal but necessary therapy. Some of the specific drugs would be changed from what I'd previously received as it was pointless giving the same drugs again when the disease had become so active so very quickly.

The junior doctor told me that before more treatment was given I would require a blood transfusion. As a consequence of all the treatment and all of the subsequent needles, it was becoming increasingly more difficult to locate good veins. The veins in my upper limbs were proving somewhat unresponsive, so after a third attempt to gain venous access, the needle for the blood transfusion was inserted into my foot.

This, of course, restricted my mobility and I was stuck lying on top of the bed. After the blood transfusion, the same needle was flushed with saline and used for my chemotherapy, although the toxic poison was infused through a different line. Unfortunately for me, despite a different cocktail of drugs, the treatment was pretty similar to what I had received earlier in the year and the side effects were just as I'd remember them, horrific!

Time seemed to go nowhere; it seemed to last forever. One day merged into the next with little respite from nausea and general lethargy. Chemotherapy had started again on 28 May 1976, almost one year exactly since diagnosis and treatment was planned as regularly as possible depending upon the recovery of my healthy cells.

The expectation was that the chosen chemotherapy treatment would be administered at ten-day intervals, although from time to time, ten days between treatments was simply not enough time for my healthy white cells to recover and it would be delayed a further week. This, of course, was depressing as it meant I could not see an end to my unwanted nightmare.

However, these deferrals were essential otherwise the chemotherapy could have quite easily, although indirectly, taken my life from me because if my white cell count had not increased sufficiently between treatments my immune system could not function adequately to fight off any opportunistic infection.

Of course, I had some difficulty understanding this concept and I was very frustrated as any delays simply prolonged my agony. All I wanted to do was get on with it so that, hopefully, I could put whatever treatment was planned behind me, yet the unforgiving chemotherapy left no part of me untouched.

One morning I awoke to discover a weird rash covering the left side of my body, with pain like electrical impulses shocking my feeble frame. The doctor quickly diagnosed Shingles. The ruthless consequences of cancer treatment increased my mental anguish at yet another setback. I did not want to be receiving chemotherapy, but what choice.

My sanity was saved somewhat by reading about the social injustices and the attempted destruction of the Lakota. It made me realise that there is always someone worse than I was. I loved reading about the culture of the Sioux nation and I still had hopes of visiting Wounded Knee someday. My sleep pattern was not the best the majority of the time, but the shingles infection was causing additional problems, my mind was now in overdrive thinking that this nightmare was never going to end.

What the hell was happening to my body? And when, if ever, would I regain control? I was given some medication and told to restrict myself to the house, which further impacted my quality of life. My biggest problem was the suppression of my normal thoughts, the inability to rationalise or comprehend why this was happening.

The weeks came and went, each day merged into the next and time was of little relevance any longer; the hospital setting became my second home and the staff part of my extended family. Despite that supportive network and, of course, not forgetting my biological family, chemotherapy treatment was no easier to accept psychologically than it was to receive physically.

There was an uneasy nervousness, a predictable fear leading up to every treatment, knowing fine well that following on from the chemotherapy my body no longer had any respect for what it was that I wanted it to do, it was controlled by the effects of the lifesaving drugs. It was as if my body was bereft of vitality, the vigour drained from within by an unrelenting attack.

The known consequences made it far less easy to accept, the waiting and anticipation of the side effects made life intolerable for a teenager in the 70's. Would there ever be an end to this purgatory?

I felt as though I was becoming a submissive entity with nothing more than an unheard voice. I had no concerns about the physical care I was receiving but my views, feelings or wishes were never considered and although my best interests were always at the forefront, what about my concerns and my needs, the loss of my identity and my worries, who would address these things?

A cloud of blackness would obscure my mind when I least expected and I found it a difficult demon to control. There were no support groups, no specialist nurses. Almost no one was willing to speak with me about cancer, fear of addressing the psychological unrest it was causing me; the risk it was posing to my existence. It felt like a one-man battle and I did not believe that I was winning this most important war.

Eventually, some five months down the line and the infernal cocktail of treatment was thankfully once again complete. However, now that the treatment was again terminated I started to plan my return to full-time employment and more importantly, attending the next Hawkwind concert. The latter took place in September 1976 at Newcastle City Hall and it would prove a spectacular event with an equally amazing light show to match the fantastic space rock that only Hawkwind could provide.

Additionally, the band's tour was still in full swing around the country and after this show, I was determined to ensure I saw them again. Therefore I arranged the necessary payment for the scheduled performance of Hawkwind at the famous Hammersmith Odeon the following month. I planned to make my way to the big city and demonstrate my support for the band.

Less than a week later that all-important ticket arrived, making me wonder if life was finally returning to normal. Once again, it would not be too long before I got the answer, but sadly not the answer I expected. I was back at work and the Readhead's shipyard in South Shields was preparing to close down and transfer its workforce to other yards along the River Tyne.

I was no exception and I was allocated a place at Swan Hunters at Wallsend. I remember my first day as if it were yesterday. As I walked into the new department, my hair still absent, a concrete reminder that my health was far from certain, someone's offensive comment to another person was just a little too loud and I overheard his sarcastic criticism of my strange hairstyle.

I was hurt and offended that another man could make light of my current predicament. Without a pause in my stride, I continued along pretending that I had not heard. As I walked, I thought of the proud Lakota Sioux warriors and their long threads of hair, which were such an important part of their own identity. Mine had been too, but it had been taken from me by a hidden scourge.

Only a week later, in total despair I knew I had to cancel my trip to London as once again, I was aware of those tell-tale signs of recurrence of cancer and the associated feelings that went hand in hand with them. I knew that it would not be possible to make the long journey to London feeling the way I did, tired and emotionally on edge, those drenching night sweats informing me that my unwanted accomplice was yet again returning for a further visit.

I had missed Newcastle United beat Stoke City by a single goal in our last game – and now sitting in my bedroom, staring at my unused ticket for the Hammersmith Odeon left me tearful and frustrated and once again wondering what the immediate future had in store for me. My next appointment was a few weeks away and in all honesty, I should have contacted the hospital to bring it forward as I knew exactly what was occurring deep within my body.

Instead, I foolishly waited, now completely bewildered and mentally unstable, near to a complete psychological breakdown.

I went to bed and lay across the duvet and closed my eyes, hoping to sleep. But the dominant demons were there in a flash. They hounded my thoughts, controlled my mind and reminded me of my life-threatening disease that continued to circulate in my body. The entity I could not control insisted on invading my psychological wellbeing, tipping it into imbalance.

Feeling depressed and isolated I trudged along to my scheduled appointment early in November 1976 more terrified than ever as to what management strategy would now be initiated. Frustratingly, it was my first clinic appointment since completing the last chemotherapy and although deep down I knew what was happening, I paradoxically prayed that I would get a clean bill of health.

It's crazy how as individuals we try to convince ourselves that things are going well and I desperately wanted to be well. Sadly and as expected my worst fears were realised, they confirmed that I had a third relapse and explained that there had been only a partial response to the chemotherapy. This came as no surprise at all, but it was the worst news I could wish to hear.

A lymph node was quite evident in my right axilla accompanied by others in my chest and I was told, as I expected, that more treatment would be required. I was, perhaps for the first time in my life, speechless, gutted, bewildered and confused as to where we go from here as I had pinned so much hope on the last chemotherapy that I had reluctantly accepted; my immediate response was one of anger.

I now felt more vulnerable than ever before, I also felt that perhaps, as a believer in destiny my end was in sight. So here I was again, I had scratched and dragged my way to the top, only to be cruelly pushed back to the bottom of this rollercoaster of emotional and physical disturbance. Dark thoughts circling in my subconscious left me embarrassed by an inclination of ending my own life.

Mentally weakened by this expected news, I thought of a simple way to end my torture and indeed, my life. But how and who would find me? I cried with self-pity, I sobbed with anger and frustration. I knew that I was not strong enough to end it all, to leave a legacy for my parents and my sister that would surely haunt them forever.

In my despair, my thoughts turned to the Lakota Sioux struggles and exploitation over the decades and their pride and steely determination was an attribute that had and would inspire me. The Lakota men would often paint their faces for personal protection before they went into battle with an enemy.

But the ceremonial culture of face painting was more than that, the chosen colours were of individual choice, intended to harmonise that persons dreams and visions. My battle was once again about to begin, I needed to put to one side the demons that lurked in the canyons of my mind and visualise my future and recognise the dreams I needed to attain.

Despite feeling very much alone, I was mentally strengthened by the thought that I was accompanied on my journey by the Lakota Sioux; dismissing the weak and destructive thoughts of suicide for the time being.

My fragile emotions and worries would belong to me and me alone as I felt that my parents and sister did not deserve to have to share this burden, a burden I couldn't manage myself. I knew how difficult my family were finding the whole ordeal and subsequently, I kept this personal turmoil inside as a protective factor in favour of them.

Of course, in hindsight that was a mistake as I struggled constantly to deal with the fears and strange dilemmas that would invade my mind daily, questions my subconscious would ask of me, questions I would refuse to answer. I had no answers to the myriad of self-posed questions and, in reality; it would have helped if I'd shared some of that responsibility.

After all, this wasn't just my cancer, it was affecting the entire family and they deserved the opportunity to help me, yet in absolute naivety, I denied them that chance and also myself the support that it would have brought with it. I suppose, in essence, the fact remains that there is no preparation for the fight against cancer, whether it is you the individual or a member of your family.

No one person can say what you should or shouldn't do; it remains the ultimate discovery of your inner self. A discovery that is made during the lonely and unpredictable road of the cancer journey and I was no exception.

This was the third relapse and had dire consequences. Once again, I began to acknowledge and yet at the same time, question my mortality, would I ever be in a position to father a child and see them grow up, had I seen Hawkwind perform for the last time, would I ever get to Wounded Knee?

My mind was filled with the never-ending worry as to exactly what fate had in store for me and concerns as to whether this disease would end my life. Questions rolled around my mind almost constantly and, yet, no one could offer any answers. My fate was woven into the intricate tapestry of life.

Perhaps my biggest problem was the fact that as a young and immature man I had always chosen not to discuss much of my illness or even talk about the savage games played out in my mind to anyone.

From the beginning, I had made the conscious decision to keep my thoughts, my fears and my questions to myself; aware that my parents who had colluded with the doctor to withhold information about my illness were struggling to understand and confront the fact that their son had cancer, a life-limiting disease.

# Chapter 6
# Merry Christmas

I first met Dr Bozzino, a Consultant Oncologist and also Dr Atkinson, a Specialist Registrar, when they took over my care from Dr Sheppard as he had accepted a new Consultancy in Australia. Dr Bozzino proposed that radiotherapy should be utilised as a treatment modality.

The medical team knew very well that I was opposed to more chemotherapy and although many may see it as my weakness, I simply could not have tolerated anymore of the infernal solution that had desecrated my entire body, especially as there was no guarantee that further chemotherapy would work.

Radiotherapy would, of course, also bring with it unknown challenges but, at the moment, I was just relieved that there was an alternative treatment available to me and one which, I thought, would not give me the dreadful side effects I had from the chemotherapy; at least that was my perception, my paranoid fears.

I was asked to make my way once again to Newcastle General Hospital to get prepared for radiotherapy and I was told that this treatment would be delivered as an outpatient and that an ambulance would take me back and forth to Newcastle each day, Monday to Friday for five weeks.

The consultant explained that radiotherapy is a treatment that is given to localised disease that is to say, it is aimed at getting rid of cancer in one specific area, whereas chemotherapy is a systemic option, it would get into every nook and cranny of the human anatomy. That was the main reason why radiotherapy had not been considered for my condition before now; they needed a treatment that would attack the widespread nature of my cancer.

Why on earth this was never explained to me months ago is anyone's guess; it would have made perfect sense and perhaps would have softened my anger at not being considered for radiotherapy before now. From a cynical viewpoint, I wondered if they thought that as a young adolescent I was not capable of comprehending this simple explanation, but that quickly became history as I focused on starting radiotherapy.

Radiotherapy is given similarly to a simple x-ray; the fundamental difference being that a much larger dose of radiation is used. However, it isn't just a case of aiming a beam of radiation at the desired area; special precautions have to be taken as this type of radiation could cause long term damage to my body.

In the first instance, special metal blocks were made to protect my lungs as the damaging rays of ionising radiation could cause permanent damage to those organs. This type of radiotherapy is called mantle irradiation. The first dose of radiotherapy was an absolute breeze taking a few minutes to deliver.

I had my skin marked, similar to a Lakota warrior which amused me, although the difference was that I felt anything but a warrior. However, this was another link to my Lakota friends, who knew nothing of my plight or their hidden support of my psychological battle, the Lakota friends whom I had never met— The Lakota Sioux who were thousands of miles away, yet, they were close to my heart.

These markings allowed radiographers to position me in exactly the correct place on the treatment couch for each of the daily treatments. Of course, like most of the treatments for cancer, the side effects were often more potent than the actual disease and radiotherapy was no exception, as, just like chemotherapy, it would damage healthy cells at the same time that it destroyed lymphoma cells too.

Unknown to me and my naive intellect, the treatment, similar to chemotherapy, would prove not to be without side effects. It had been me, who had persistently argued and insisted on having radiotherapy having seen all of those other chaps receive this form of treatment at Newcastle. As I saw it, it had seemed free of side effects.

The first three weeks of radiotherapy went without any problem; however, like chemotherapy treatment, radiotherapy also affects healthy cells and eventually, the treatment began to take its savage toll on my young and innocent body. At first, these side effects crept up on me very gradually. Firstly, the tiredness left me so fatigued that I would feel the need to sleep for at least a couple of hours on my return from hospital.

Secondly, my throat became hoarse and I had difficulty swallowing. Soon afterwards the sickness started and proved just as difficult to control as the chemotherapy-induced sickness. The plan was for twenty-three treatments consisting of a total of 3436 rads (a measure of radiation), to the chest and neck, with a final booster of 500 rads to the right axilla, the area that refused to succumb to the chemotherapy treatment.

At the Newcastle hospital where the radiotherapy was given the small waiting area was crammed wall to wall with patient's waiting to receive their treatment. A constant production line is exactly what you do not want when you are feeling low in mood, tired and just wanting to be anywhere other than a hospital.

At times, I felt trapped in a permanent nightmare with no ending, thinking that if I died that would be a release, but instead I'm alive and stuck with this unbearable burden of cancer. Christmas 1976 was, without a doubt, the worst Christmas of my entire life.

My get up and go, got up of its own volition and went, leaving me bereft of vigour, drained of enthusiasm; in the depths of despair and persecuted by an illness I could not see and, more importantly, that I had no control over. Ironically, I was now learning to respect this potential killer disease that was proving rather difficult to eradicate.

Its persistence to return and invade my body, its refusal to respond to conventional treatment and the difficulty modern medicine had in ridding society of this disease.

To make matters worse I found that my appetite was perhaps the worst thing affected, perhaps due to the constant feeling of nausea. Everything I tried to eat tasted like soggy cardboard and my mam was concerned and tried all kinds of tempting dishes with little success. She even went out and bought a build-up drink to try and tempt my taste buds.

Now here is a strange concept, if I am not eating then the last thing I would want is some bland, tasteless unappetising drink, even though it was supposed to deliver the nutritional support I was lacking. Sadly the drink was indeed bland and tasteless and something that succeeded in exacerbating my nausea. As much as I appreciated mam's attempt to build me up, that approach was simply not for me.

To make matters worse, as the radiotherapy exerted its effect on the disease in my chest, the pains I experienced were excruciating. They would manifest when I least expected them and caused me to freeze with discomfort and fear,

fear that this was the progression of the lymphoma. I had been prescribed strong painkillers, but even these had unwanted side effects.

I became constipated and they caused my head to spin as if I had consumed an entire bottle of my favourite Bourbon, 'Jim Beam'. The pain would be worse at night when I was alone, compounded by the silence, the darkness, the isolation and, of course, my trepidation of what lay ahead.

I felt lost and persecuted by an uninvited entity inside my body that refused to leave me. Radiotherapy continued until 28 January 1977, through what was a freezing winter with plenty of snow on the ground.

Trying to get motivated, I remember going for short walks in the snow and I think in all honesty it was at this stage that I felt sorrier for myself than at any other moment in time. I was aware that all of my friends would be out enjoying themselves and although they regularly called in during the day to see me, night-time was different as it was a constant reminder that I was not living a normal life.

I was isolated from society, unable to participate in the activities of any normal teenager, battling an unseen disease that refused to release me from its deathly grip. I was still not eating and I began to lose weight which concerned not only my parents but also the medical staff. At one point, Dr Bozzino confessed that he was considering stopping the radiotherapy due to his concerns over my weight loss, although in his wisdom he eventually decided against that course of action.

I previously mentioned that during my darkest moments I had thoughts of ending my life and you might wonder how often I had felt that way. I can say that it was on more than one occasion and that is a fact that I am not ashamed to admit. The thought of ending my own life did not just cause me personal grief and consternation, it made me feel guilty as I knew the devastation it would cause my family.

Without any warning whatsoever, dark thoughts would wander, unopposed and uninvited, through the canyons of my mind—a cloak of uncertainty and suggestions that my young head was unable to understand or comprehend. Not for the first time, I turned to the inspirational Lakota Sioux and in particular, a Holy man called 'Black Elk'.

His editorial about his persecution and his resolve and his unexplained visions, which gave him direction in life, spurred me on and out of the spiralling depressive mind-set. Deep inside my head, his words resonated and something inside me said, you will survive. Regardless, I am not sure whether I would have had the courage to carry out that fateful deed.

Unlike today, when I was treated with radiotherapy you were not allowed to wash the area being treated and subsequently, I developed a large 'tide' mark around the back of my neck where my collars would rub. Additionally, I had not had a bath for the entire duration of the treatment and my hair had not been washed for the same period of time.

The suggestion was that both your hair and skin could be washed with talcum powder. Of course, I am sure that everyone can appreciate that this does not work the same as good old soap and water. I felt filthy and lord only knows what pungent aroma I would be giving off? Joking aside, no one ever gave me the slightest indication that there was a problem with my hygiene and it was also the time of the good old 'Brut' aftershave adverts on television and Christmas had brought me my fair share of the smelly cologne.

Therefore, every morning religiously during the radiotherapy days, I would splash it all over! After completing my radiotherapy, I had to wait a further fourteen days before I could bathe, as the radiation was still effective on my skin for that duration. Eventually, though, the day arrived and my mam had filled the most inviting bath I had ever wished for.

Tentatively I dipped my toes in as if I was an alien visiting a strange land and having my first experience of water. I lay there smiling to myself and soaked my skin to a prune until the water became only tepid. Despite my long and relaxing soak, the tide mark remained for some weeks thereafter and this was a great source of ridicule by my mam and she made it her business to tell everyone about the now-famous tide mark around my neck.

Despite the seriousness and gravity of the situation, it was good to laugh. I hadn't done a lot of laughing up to this point. I felt alive, content and almost normal but not quite.

As the weeks progressed I began to get stronger and stronger and began to get the urge to return to work. I also began to dream about visiting America and an Indian reservation. I had been keeping in regular contact with Aunty Mary and the offer to visit was permanently on the table. My hospital visits continued at monthly intervals to monitor my blood counts and undergo the usual physical examinations which were a pre-requisite to every visit.

As the time progressed during these, my formative years, I matured rather quickly and appreciated that life was not only important but also precious. I soon deduced that for the majority of people, life was taken for granted and yet more than anyone I now knew how special life was. Seeing individual after individual abuse themselves, I had no doubt, that had illness not intervened, and then I too would have been just another person who did not respect the sanctity of life.

I was slowly but surely earning more and more respect for this cancer, but equally accepting that it was teaching me a very valuable lesson about life; enjoy it while you can as we won't be here forever. Things went well for some weeks but, soon, things took an almost expected downward plunge. Some five weeks after completing my radiotherapy I discovered a lump under my left arm and knew exactly what this meant, lymphoma! More importantly, it also meant the prospect of more treatment.

This represented the fourth relapse and immediately my mood sunk to a new low, imagining that perhaps my life was not destined to be a long one, I desperately did not want to allow these depressive feelings to take over my mind and once again I searched for motivation. It is very important to highlight that my family were a vitally significant component in my life, especially during my illness.

But the stories I read about the Lakota people and to a lesser extent Hawkwind gave me the element of escapism and distraction that I was seeking; a connection with spirituality and with my soul, which is difficult to explain to someone who has not faced their own mortality. My mood followed peaks and troughs of uncontrollable dimensions of emotional instability.

Twelve months earlier I would have shuddered at the thought of more chemotherapy and the potential dangers that it brought with it. But now, I was desperately hoping more treatment would be offered as I was determined to cling on to life as I knew that I had so much to live for. I also had my family to consider.

They were right behind me and supported me to the very best of their ability. They felt my pain and shared my anguish as if it was their own. I knew I had their undivided support, but, equally, I knew that refusing further treatment would be the ultimate self-destruction that might also destroy them. I never saw Dr Sheppard again, but my parents did!

Now, it's quite easy to be critical of my parents and their collusion with the medical establishment, but I know for certain how they too struggled mentally with my cancer diagnosis. They were or tried to be very protective, whilst at the same time as a twenty-year-old I was trying to adjust to life outside of my sickness.

I was desperate to get out and about, not just to see live music, but to socialise with my dependable and supportive friends. My life was still of course governed by cancer and the effects of the treatment and I was well aware that my frailty was far from over. However, I accepted and knew that to a man my friends would watch over me whenever we were together and I also appreciated the confidence and comfort that their friendship and support brought me.

But, it was a peculiar emotion I experienced; whilst their support sometimes felt like protectionism, they gave this with the best of intentions. I felt that I had lost my adolescence. I felt that because of their protection I was not normal.

Unknown to me and as if they had not learned anything from the first time, my parents met with Dr Sheppard one afternoon when they were told that it was not now possible to control this aggressive lymphoma. He further explained that from a medical prognosis, it was only a matter of time until I succumbed to this unresponsive cancer.

The plan, therefore, from that moment in time was a palliative treatment which was intended to control my symptoms, but significantly would not cure the lymphoma! The decision was made without my consent, nothing new there then! However, here is the ethical dilemma, if I had been told that I was not expected to survive, would I have accepted the offer of further chemotherapy? I suspect not.

One important factor in the history of my illness is the use of complementary therapy. My mam had been reading about this wonder root called Ginseng and the significant improvement it could make to the human body. The book she had read claimed that the root could improve life and rid the body of many conditions and ailments, although I do not believe it claimed to treat cancer.

Nevertheless, she duly went out and bought a supply of this herb and each day I would regimentally take one capsule. Until her dying day, mam insisted this herbal root played a significant role in my recovery. Previously, when I returned to work following the radiotherapy, I struggled to complete a full five days and, at times, I would only manage two or three days.

Management was first class and on the whole very supportive; their suggestion to me was to come in when you can get in. I was never sure whether mam or dad had spoken to anyone at work to inform them of how ill I was. However, I truly appreciated the fact that work was flexible with my hours because for me it was a valuable element, both from a financial perspective but also to normalise my life again and I endeavoured to get into work at every opportunity.

Despite my relentless tiredness my thoughts were focused on the next Hawkwind tour, where would that be and would I manage to get there? At my next clinic appointment, Dr Bozzino spoke to me directly and listened to me, giving me the time to ask specific questions.

I am not saying that Dr Sheppard had not spoken to me previously, he had done and he was an excellent doctor. I just felt that he mostly collaborated with my parents about my disease and my management. After all, this was my illness and I felt he had previously attempted, although well-intentioned, to take it away from me and remove my role in the decision-making process.

Dr Bozzino was an articulate and pleasant gentleman, who made me feel very relaxed. His time was my time and importantly, he made time to ensure that I was able to ask all the questions that I needed. His eternal optimism was heart-warming, even though he knew something that I did not. Dr Atkinson would also have a special place in my heart for reasons that will soon become apparent.

He was a tall Englishman with an excellent disposition, someone who enjoyed a good laugh, someone I could relate to, empathetic and professional and I developed the utmost respect for both men. At that consultation I was told that I'd had a fair response to the radiotherapy, but there was a node under my arm and some lymph nodes deep in the abdomen which had not been treated by the radiotherapy and, therefore, needed to be targeted by other treatment.

Unbeknown to me, what this amounted to was palliative chemotherapy to improve my quality of life, but wouldn't cure my cancer. This was something that had already been discussed with my parents but not me. Whether Dr Bozzino and Dr Atkinson were aware of that collusion between Dr Sheppard and my parents I was never sure, I prefer to believe that they did not, but honestly suspect they did.

I was told that I was to have weekly injections, which would be almost free from side effects. This was certainly something that impressed me immediately, but was this possible, no side effects from chemotherapy? I doubted that very much. I later learned that the reason there were fewer side effects was that this type of treatment is weaker as it is only intended to resolve some of my symptoms and push the disease into the background, not to cure it.

I was asked to go for a coffee until the drug could be ordered from the pharmacy and I was happy to oblige, I had received a lot of information from these two doctors and, most importantly, I was being involved in the decision-making process and as such, I saw no reason to question this next course of action.

I trotted around to the WRVS coffee bar and, an hour or so later, one of the nurses came looking for me to say that Dr Bozzino was now ready for me and I was subsequently whisked straight back into the consulting room that I know so very well. Dr Bozzino had a butterfly needle in the back of my hand and secured into position before I knew it.

The drug, called Vinblastine was administered in no time at all and the needle was swiftly removed and I was on my way home before I knew it. Over the next three months, I attended the outpatient department to see either Dr Atkinson or Dr Bozzino and to receive my Vinblastine injection. The dose would be dependent upon the response of my white cells; on occasions, I would get a reduced dose but at other times I would get no treatment to allow my healthy cells to recover.

Most importantly, this was all explained to me. At my appointment on 9 June 1977, there was no detectable disease but I did have specific problems with my arms. I was experiencing pain in the left and right arms and on examination, my reflexes were absent in the left and reduced in the right.

Furthermore, I was having a strange pain, a toothache like attack from time to time. My question was, was this a result of the drug, known to cause peripheral neuropathy and jaw pain or was it due to active disease again? I was given no indication as to what was causing these strange manifestations; but equally, I did not ask the obvious question, was this caused by the lymphoma? My sanity would be unable to cope with the answer I dreaded more than any other.

The Vinblastine was continued at a full dose with the period between treatments lengthened to twenty-one day intervals. Three weeks later I was experiencing pain and an absence of reflexes in my biceps, wrists and left triceps plus my eyesight was becoming blurred. Dr Atkinson assures me that this was probably a result of the chemotherapy and, therefore, suggested that I have a break from treatment until these symptoms resolve.

Furthermore and most encouragingly, he told me that, As far as he could tell, there was no evidence of any disease. I appreciated his reassurance, but as there had been so many setbacks, my mind raced with the fear that the symptoms were due to the disease and my anxiety reminded me that I was still terrified of a return of cancer.

After a few weeks without treatment, I returned to the hospital for a check-up and consideration of my future treatment management. As I sat in the waiting area prepared for the worst but hoping for the best, my mind was occupied with questions without answers. What a relief when Dr Atkinson tells me that my blood is fine and after a physical examination, that there were no lymph glands to be detected.

The symptoms previously reported had subsided and I was now convinced that perhaps that was due to the chemotherapy. Dr Atkinson decided that the Vinblastine injections that were planned should be completed.

Of course, I had still not been privy to the knowledge that this treatment was designed at being palliative in nature and even though I have the utmost respect for the doctors and nurses who got me through the most difficult time of my life and everyone who nursed and cajoled me through the real possibility of an early death, I am still to this day bewildered that there was so much collusion in respect to what was my illness, my treatment, my future.

I simply have to accept that it was done with the best of intentions, to do otherwise would cause me to self-destruct.

# Chapter 7
# Heading to America

Before July 1977, I had never had the good fortune to visit another country, but I now had an ideal opportunity to visit America as part of my recuperation. Preparing for the trip would keep my mind occupied and I was filled with excitement and, of course, anticipation of a very welcome break from the intensity of almost constant cancer treatment.

Fatigue was, of course, ever-present. It was a daily reminder that I was a cancer patient with an uncertain future and had spent so much time as an imprisoned hospital patient with an immune system as fragile as eggshells, an enslaved outpatient back and forth to the hospital like a yo-yo.

The side effects of treatment seemed to be ever-present over the past two years and quite simply my get up and go had left me a long time ago, corrupted by the indiscriminate chemotherapy and I had little idea of when it might return, if at all. Despite my fatigue, I was determined to visit the country that had held my fascination for so long and helped me sustain some sanity during many difficult months.

Over the time of my illness, I had managed to save a few pounds that would subsidise my American trip and during the planning stages, I eagerly scoured the press in the hope of finding a trip that would allow me to see the real stateside. I planned to spend four weeks in North Carolina with Aunty Mary and her family.

My travel companion would be another of mam's sisters, Aunty Kathleen. Like me, this would be her first trip to America. In respect of my health, despite still feeling the effects of the treatment, I had not given a second thought to how it might affect my trip. As far as I was concerned there would be no problems, especially as I had fully discussed the holiday with Dr Atkinson and he felt it would be good for me.

He had arranged the appropriate correspondence for me to take which highlighted my medical history. Giving this important document little thought I placed it into my suitcase ready to take. The planning was now all completed, the day of departure was upon us and so, in late July 1977, we headed off to North Carolina with huge aspirations, but also cautious trepidation.

Arriving by car at Manchester airport, I felt my heart skip a beat as we drove into the airport and a jumbo jet appeared to hover above us, almost motionless as it came into land. I had simply not realised the size of these machines. As my heart bumped and my mouth became dry, I started to feel a degree of anxiety about the imminent flight.

Fortunately, there was no time for nerves as we were slightly behind schedule and we needed to check in immediately, no sooner had we done this we had to make our way into the departure lounge and before we knew it we were boarding the aircraft. It was all done so quickly that my anxiety was forgotten.

The whole experience was something special; it was my first trip abroad and an opportunity to leave the cancer experience behind. Touching down in New York I was very excited, even though we still had another flight from New York down to Greensboro, our final destination. The hustle and bustle of New York City certainly did not impress me and I found it no different from any other cosmopolitan city.

In contrast, when we touched down in Greensboro and the cabin door was opened, I was taken aback by the humidity which caught the back of my throat. This was awesome and I was impressed like never before. I felt like standing at the top of those stairs and like a head of state, waving to those individuals I could not see in the main building, all those people who knew nothing of my torture during the past two years and what this trip ultimately meant to me.

Not long ago and my future was so unsure, yet here I was standing on the tarmac of Greensboro airport, a completely different world from the one I had left behind. Collecting our bags, we met Aunty Mary and Uncle Jerry outside of customs control and I have to admit to being somewhat overawed by the whole experience.

Outside in the car park was Uncle Jerry's Pontiac Grand Prix and, as you would expect in America, it was huge a vehicle, a true gas-guzzler. Riding in style from the airport took around 45 minutes although, such was my excitement and it only seemed like a few moments since we got into the car.

The drive from the airport had left me feeling like a VIP, but I could not help but notice the extremes of wealth. On one hand, there were these luxurious beautiful homes, many of which had swimming pools and in stark contrast, there were others that were little other than wooden huts, looking as if the slightest gust of wind would blow them over.

Arriving at Pine Knolls, Kernersville and the house overlooked a magnificent golf course, although such was the summer heat and humidity that the grass was completely scorched. The inside of the house was, of course, air-conditioned and very palatial and as far removed from my own home as you could imagine.

Yet despite the obvious wealth, I was more than content with our small council house back in South Shields, particularly as my illness had taught me that you should appreciate anything that you have and money does not buy your health. I was greeted by some of my cousins and it felt like I had known them forever.

Over tea, we talked and talked about many different subjects, not least my illness and after a while, I had decided to put on a pair of shorts and take a walk around the estate. I had only strolled a few hundred yards, past the tennis courts when I heard the distinct southern drawl of '*look at that pair of skinny milk bottles*'.

Naturally, they referred to my white lower limbs. Legs that had not seen the light of day for I do not know how long and which were still recovering from the destructive attack of lymphoma and the chemotherapy used to treat it. Those sarcastic voices, of course, were not to know about my secret illness and without malice, I had a little smile to myself, after all, I would have done the same thing.

Four glorious weeks in America was highlighted by a trip to the Great Smokey Mountains and then into Oconaluftee Village, the Cherokee Indian Reservation and the pinnacle of my visit. Pulling up in one of the car parks we were greeted by a Native American Indian, sadly he was artificially made up especially for the tourist and he immediately stretched out his sun-baked hand waiting for the dollar bills that would allow us to take his photograph.

Although there were lots of authenticities, there was also an awful lot of tourist junk The feeling of pride that the Native Americans had irrespective of their plight and the atrocious way that the American model had oppressed and undermined them was admirable. This truly was a humbling experience, a visit that lived up to all my expectations.

These great people had almost been wiped out by the greed and avarice of unlawful European settlers over many centuries and, yet, they had lost none of their resolve; something I could associate with in my battle against lymphoma.

Driving from Oconaluftee Village the journey through the mountains was breathtakingly beautiful and certainly something that mere words could not do justice to here. In a small clearing, we stopped the car and found a small gurgling stream. Without hesitation and almost instinctively, I knelt and sipped the crystal clear virgin water of Oconaluftee River.

As we were driving back down the winding road of the Smokey Mountains the heavens opened and raindrops that were the size of golf balls bounced off the car. I asked Uncle Jerry about visiting the Lakota tribal lands at Wounded Knee; he simply laughed and told me that 'Pine Ridge Reservation was in South Dakota some 1500 miles away, more than a 24-hour drive'.

Still, silently I promised myself one day I would visit Wounded Knee and the proud Lakota people who had unknowingly supported me through my battle with cancer.

During my stay in the Deep South, I met some wonderful people, so genuine and friendly and did they know how to cook. That good old southern food is second to none as was the hospitality. We did an awful lot of travelling and saw some beautiful places, the memories of which would stay with me forever.

My cousins Karen, David, Shelley, Scott and Charles helped make the holiday a memorable one. One particular night Charles and I visited a night club and as we went in everyone was taken by my English accent, especially a bunch of Hells Angels who looked quite fearsome but ironically, turned out to be big Hawkwind fans and very friendly.

All the way to America to bump into Hawkwind fans, now that's impressive, now that's fate! Naturally, we talked music, shared a joint and discussed the experience of seeing Hawkwind live, as most of them hadn't done so; they had many questions about Hawkwind that I was only too pleased to answer.

There were many parties organised and, indeed, at one of these I met a young girl called Melissa. After chatting most of the night I walked her back to her car and without thinking gave her a long lingering kiss that seemed to last forever. We arranged to meet the next day and again the next.

She was gorgeous and I thought I was in love for the first time, as I had previously with the Mayor's daughter and her image filled my thoughts for months after my return home. I firmly believe that the entire experience had a significant impact on my health and certainly played a part in my recovery, not least psychologically. The experience was so impressive that I promised to return the following year.

Returning to England I was more than apprehensive of my next requisite hospital appointment as I was feeling so very well, in fact, better than I had for many months, but would I feel as well when I came out of the consultation? My reflexes were still not what they should be although, in all honesty, I had not realised any deficit and I had no specific symptoms.

I waltzed into the consulting room and took my place on the examination couch, suddenly the butterflies were evident as Dr Atkinson strolled in, his usual smile stretched across his bearded face he asked how the holiday had gone and naturally, I was only too pleased to tell him. It had been over five weeks since my last treatment and Dr Atkinson was keen to continue with the Vinblastine injections.

My first thought was, when would it stop? The proposal was that a further six injections should be given at two weekly intervals. This I could accept as Hawkwind were once again on the road and heading to Newcastle in September and I certainly planned to be the first in the queue for a ticket! On this occasion, I would take my sister Allyson with me.

Allyson loved David Cassidy and other teenybopper music, so I was dubious as to her reaction to Hawkwind—but she knew my passion for the band and she was keen to accompany me. After the gig, she was as enthusiastic as me, although her interest was not sustained, most importantly she had enjoyed the night of live space rock and it gave me great pleasure to take her along to see such an important event.

As regards my acceptance of the proposed treatment plan, aside from my desire to see Hawkwind again, now that I had come this far it would have been foolish to stop treatment against medical advice, especially as I had endured chemotherapy so horribly worse than this and any argument I had against this particular treatment really would not be a strong one.

I also agreed with Dr Atkinson's opinion of more chemotherapy, simply because I had absolute faith in his clinical judgement. Dr Atkinson explained that on completion of the Vinblastine injections I need to be admitted to Newcastle General Hospital for in-depth investigations to determine whether there was any disease still evident.

I agreed to his request but emphasised that I could not be in hospital on the 20 September or the 5 October. On those dates, I had two significant and most important appointments, the first at the City Hall in Newcastle and then followed by another journey to London, this time onto the Hammersmith Odeon to see a certain band called Hawkwind.

There was no doubt that my inspirational band had kept me going through so many emotional and difficult tribulations that I would travel anywhere to see them; in addition, I knew that one day I had to make a journey to South Dakota and Wounded Knee. The Lakota people without knowing had also supported me through the worst adventure of my life.

True to his word I was admitted to Newcastle General Hospital at the end of November for a week of invasive tests and investigations which would make or break my future, tests that could break my spirit once and for all. Alighting from the lift at ward 38, I noticed plenty of familiar faces from the nursing staff but my kindred spirit Tom was nowhere to be seen.

Sadly, I would never see him again. The ward was quiet and I was allocated a cubicle, which was preferential treatment compared to my previous visit. That same day I had a bone scan and also a series of x-rays. Of course, blood samples were taken almost daily.

I had made my way up to Newcastle, which is about a thirty-minute drive from South Shields in my little car, a white Hillman Imp which I had parked proudly outside of the hospital and although ward 38 was on the fifth floor, I could see the car from the toilet window.

(This is an important point worth remembering.) The following day I was scheduled for a lymphangiogram investigation. This was the second occasion I would have this test; the first time was part of my diagnostic investigations and confirmed my cancer as Lymphoma. This assessment of my lymphatic system was undertaken at a time before the availability of CT scans.

I was taken into the treatment room and made comfortable on the examination couch; my feet were cleaned with an antiseptic solution, then local anaesthetic was injected between my first two toes and it certainly did sting when it was administered. On the top of each foot, an incision was made approximately an inch in length from, which the lymphatic channel could be accessed to infuse a special blue coloured solution over two hours.

The infusion would circulate my lymphatic system and allow a series of x-rays to be taken that would make a dedicated inspection and ultimately determine whether there was any remaining lymphoma present. The blue dye turned not only my urine blue but also gave my skin a blue tinge for days afterwards.

Following the procedure, my feet were stitched and I was expected to remain in a wheelchair for at least twenty-four hours. However, following the lymphangiogram investigation in my infinite wisdom, I decided to go and check my car to ensure my little motor was safe and that the battery was not flat.

I manoeuvred my wheelchair into the lift and down to the ground floor and, in a few moments I was out into the open air, steering my wheelchair as if I was Lewis Hamilton negotiating a Grand Prix circuit. The car park was slightly downhill, but in fact, it was more downhill than I realised.

Initially, it wasn't too hard to control the chair, but as it gathered more and more momentum I lost control and how I did not tip completely out of the contraption is something I will never understand. As I was rolling down the hill, I was picking up speed and unfortunately heading directly towards my pride and joy, my little car.

With little chance of stopping, there was one almighty crash into the side of the vehicle! What a spectacle, what an idiot, my biggest concern was not for my feet, not for my car and certainly not for the wheelchair, I was more concerned that someone would be looking out of a window and would have seen my calamitous performance.

I forgot the physical pain and became aware of my face beginning to flush with embarrassment as I feared someone somewhere was in hysterical laughter.

Fortunately, my feet, the car and the wheelchair were none the worse for the crazy stunt and only my pride was hurt. Cautiously, I made my way back up to the entrance of the hospital and into the lift and back onto the ward, paranoid that someone must have seen the mishap. No one ever admitted to seeing me, but I am still not convinced that some of the staff had seen the spectacle and had a dammed good laugh at my expense.

After all of the tests had been completed I was discharged home, although it would be another week before the entire test results had been collated and sent to Dr Atkinson It was going to be a very long week; an eternal wait for the most important results of my life and I would soon realise just how long seven days could feel.

Despite being at work during the day, my mind was preoccupied with the potential test results, thinking that they must be positive as I felt so well. But I had been optimistic before and on those occasions, I received news that my cancer was still in evidence; would that be the case now?

The days seemed to linger and doubt almost inevitably crept into my mind, especially as so many times in the past cancer had come sweeping back to invade my fragile body and destroy my mental stability. Dr Atkinson knew what these results meant to me and I thought that if they proved positive and in my favour, surely he would have been in touch to put me out of my mental torment.

As the days dragged on and I had not heard anything from Dr Atkinson, I began to convince myself that it must be bad news and I persuaded myself that the tests showed the presence of ongoing cancer. Night-time was undoubtedly the worst as I could not settle; my mind desperately needed the answers to those fundamental investigations.

Of course, dwelling on the negative simply fuelled my negative thoughts further. I tossed and turned, frequently getting up and going back to bed but still being unable to rest. This continued every night leading up to the hospital visit when the all-important results would be disclosed. Wide awake, yet still tired I would get up and sit reading about Black Elk, a Lakota medicine man.

Unable to focus for more than a few minutes on any reading I would eventually drop off to sleep sitting in the chair, awaking in the early hours unrefreshed and irritable. The night before my appointment, my mind was filled with doubt, pessimism and worry about what I would be told.

If it was bad news, would I be offered any more treatment and was I ready for more treatment? Could I, physically and mentally, take any more treatment after everything I had been through? After all, I had relapsed on four separate occasions, one of those relapses whilst I was receiving active chemotherapy. Why should this last treatment have been any more successful than those treatments that had gone before?

Thursday arrived and alone by choice, I made my way to the hospital anxious as never before and as always, I went straight to the blood room to have a blood test. Significantly, the blood room was directly up the corridor from where the Oncology clinic was held and as I walked sluggishly along the corridor gazing at the ground in negative anticipation, I lifted my head to see Dr Atkinson standing in the doorway.

Suddenly, my heart skipped a beat and with each beat, I felt certain my heart was going to explode out of my chest wall. My mouth was dry and I was close to tears as my fear increased. Despite being some thirty feet away he suddenly and unexpectedly threw his arms in the air and shouted at me 'You're all clear, bloody clear!'

Those five words were crystal clear and echoed around my head like a stuck gramophone record. I hear them many times in my head even today. Had I heard him correctly, had it all been a dream? Despite this fantastic news, I was somewhat bemused as to how I should react to this news, news that could not be surpassed by any lottery win.

As I drew up close to Dr Atkinson, he took my hand and firmly shook it with true commitment and graciousness, I began to fill up with emotion as the tears rolled down my cheek and I did not know what to say to my friend, my doctor who had given me such an astonishing gift. To my dying day, I will not forget that particular moment more than any other during my traumatic experience.

All of that aggressive and debilitating chemotherapy and relapse after relapse after relapse, the onslaught of Yuletide radiotherapy and failure of that treatment and finally treatment using a drug administered not with the intention of cure, but merely to control my symptoms whilst the cancer slowly robbed me of my life.

How ironic then, that this palliative drug would force my cancer into remission. I went home on an artificial high, drunk on euphoria and desperate to share my news with the world.

So that was it! My treatment was finished, I was in the clear for now and it was time to get on with the rest of my life. Naturally, regular reviews would be required and I knew deep down that I was far from out of the woods. It had been a long hard and emotional battle with a persistent disease, the treatment had taken hold of me and attacked me from every conceivable direction, not one solitary dimension of my body was spared the effects of the disease and treatment, my mind included, especially my mind.

My adolescence had been taken away and my sanity stretched to its limit. Even my testicles had shrunk to half their size as a consequence of the drugs, what a cruel and unfair legacy and something that would cause untold embarrassment in future years. My mortality had been on a knife-edge on more than one occasion and the savage side effects had pushed my body to its limits, to a cruel and unwanted place no one should ever have to visit.

Strangely, however, I felt good about the entire experience; it had taken so much from me but, bizarrely, it had given me so much in return. An appreciation of life, a focus previously unknown and a promise to myself to live my life to the full and take each day as it came; life was too short to do any other.

Sadly and now regrettably, I had refused to have any photographs taken during the entire cancer journey; the few pictures that had been snapped, I had destroyed, including the negatives as I did not want any photographic reminder of my sad experience, it was a knee jerk reaction that I now regretted.

Paradoxically, although I had a new direction and appreciation of life, my mind was permanently and painfully full of the thoughts and recollections that I desperately wanted to discard, but couldn't. Over the following twelve months, I would continue to attend the outpatients for check-ups and almost expectedly, before each visit I would be anxious about the outcome, my mind conjuring up negativity of the inner thoughts I couldn't cast aside, always fearful of being told the lymphoma is back.

The questions were always there—would I get confirmation that I'm still clear or would they be unsure and ask me to take more tests? Of course, at each visit, I would get the all-important clarification that my body was free of any signs of cancer. Between visits, I would get to see Hawkwind and once again experience the well-being, inspiration and positive vibes that they had given me during my difficult treatment.

Towards the end of 1978, I returned to America, this time to Tennessee where Aunty Mary and Uncle Jerry had moved. I would once again visit Oconaluftee Village in the Smokey Mountains and the mystical Cherokee Natives. But it was the Lakota people and Wounded Knee that I needed to visit more than anything else.

There was even a time when I thought I wanted to leave England and set up home in America and rebuild my life there, but moving to America was not, unfortunately, to be part of my fate.

My mind often fluctuated from depressive thoughts to euphoric expectations. Confusion clouded my inner thoughts; a dubious uncertainty about my future plagued my mind. Doubt, trepidation, and emotions that I did not, and could not understand, caused me to miss the final home game of the season - a thrilling three-nil defeat of Burnley. These thoughts would harass my senses for many hours of many days.

# Chapter 8
## The Joys of Parenthood

Illness had played such an integral part in my life and had at times been all-consuming that I had missed out on so much that others took for granted. Of course, when I did have the opportunity to get out and about, I preferred to travel the length and breadth of the country to see Hawkwind, to repay the support they had unknowingly delivered to me during my time of ultimate need.

They had supported me, kept me focussed at the most difficult times throughout my youth, as had the people of the great Sioux Empire. Yet still I felt that so much of my adolescence had been ruthlessly stripped from me without my consent. Adolescence for me had not been normal. How could you call a cancer affliction normal? It had, however, moulded my belief system, shown me a pathway of innocence and at the same time guilt; I was a survivor, yet survivorship would throw up more challenges. Directly, and indirectly, me and my shadow would be constant companions.

As we moved towards the end of the seventies many of my friends were already planning their respective weddings and yet I could count on one hand the girlfriends that I'd had and all were before my illness. I felt the urge to settle down, to get married and to try and normalise my life, to do exactly what society demands of us.

Sadly, that would prove to be a heartache decision as it was an unhappy and confrontational marriage that ended in divorce, although not before I would experience the joyful highs and the depths of despair as a father. Significantly like most broken marriages, I must share part of the blame for that failed relationship.

It was in 1979 that I met my first wife and, in hindsight, it was easy to see that this would never work out and I take full responsibility for that, marriage was a knee jerk reaction on my part to be the same as everyone else and be recognised as normal. For so long, I had not been able to do the things that everyone else had been able to do due to the restriction placed on me by cancer and its vice-like grip.

Not only did I miss so much of my adolescence, but I also missed the journey of discovery that is known as the opposite sex. However, in the fullness of time, my newfound girlfriend, an only child, spoiled by ageing parents, would prove to be a very jealous woman, although I would vehemently contend she never had anything or anyone to be jealous of.

In my defence and hand on heart, not once in that failed marriage did I ever give her any reason to be jealous; yet later down the years, I would be accused of having affairs with nurses, my best friend's wife and even other men, not one of these accusations held any credence or substance.

This is not the time to dwell on past mistakes however, but it is relevant as the hasty decision made as a consequence of my illness had dire consequences and affected several lives. In the first instance of our marriage, the shuddering reality of a cancer diagnosis soon raised its ugly head and it became evident that the final whistle of a cancer diagnosis never blows.

Regardless of the early marital obstacles, things were OK for a while, until talk came around to starting a family. Naturally, that was something that we both wanted. Life just isn't the same without children and we both agreed that at least two children would be ideal. From that perspective, however, nothing seemed to be happening.

After six months and, even though that was still early days, something prompted us to seek help from the family doctor. Was it her or was it me who had a problem? Or, was it that we simply had not given it enough time? I had moved away from the previous doctor's practice when I got married, so we made an appointment to see our family doctor.

He appeared very nervous when confronted by the question as to why we had not gotten pregnant. His discomfort was obvious as he squirmed in his seat and informed us that it was unlikely that we would get pregnant as the type of chemotherapy I had received some years earlier would ensure that I was completely infertile.

I was stunned and speechless, no one had ever approached this scenario and I could not recall any health care professional even intimating that this might be a problem. I felt gutted, tearful and also very angry and cheated and abused. After surviving the horrendous experience of cancer and its debilitating treatment, this just seemed like another assault and I wondered whether my cancer experience would ever end.

Cancer doesn't just stop influencing your life once treatment has been completed, it was surely influencing mine now and, believe me, I was angered. I think on reflection I was angered more by the medical fraternity than the actual disease. The disease itself could have quite literally taken my life but, instead against the odds, I had survived and had developed a healthy respect for this most unforgiving of conditions.

The doctors must have known that the treatment would cause infertility, but they failed to tell me, perhaps the truth is that they didn't expect me to survive. In addition, I did feel a huge burden of guilt for my wife. She was now in a position where she was also struggling to come to terms with this unfortunate situation, and through no fault of her own.

Yes, I was clear of the dreaded malignancy and, of course, I was grateful for that, but the bitter aftertaste took away my anticipation and determination to be a parent. A couple of months later, we decided that we would not be beaten. The answer is adoption! Unfortunately, it was not to be that easy, as following enquiries to many of the local adoption agencies we were declined without hesitation or explanation.

Even the local social services decided that because of my background of cancer we were not fit to be considered as prospective adoptive parents. Ironically, the fostering and adoption officer who had previously declined our approach to be either foster or adoptive parents left to have a baby and the new incoming Social Worker, Maggie, had been reviewing all of the old files and had discovered ours.

She later confessed to being bewildered as to why we had not been considered for, at the very least, fostering. Maggie contacted us and asked if she could come and visit. Not only was this the start of a professional relationship it was also the beginning of a great friendship.

Maggie explained that there was no reason why we could not, in the first instance foster children with a view to long term fostering and subsequently and hopefully, adoption. Maggie agreed to put the wheels in motion, explaining that references and police checks would need to be done as an integral part of this system.

In less than six months, after many interviews we went before a matching panel with the view of being considered for a fostering position with a child currently in short term placement, her name was Donna. Maggie explained that the child needed some long-term stability and she felt that we were the people to offer it.

We agreed immediately of course and plans were subsequently made for our first meeting with Donna. Trepidation is an understatement regarding the hours leading up to our rendezvous with Donna at her short-term foster home. At the foster parents home, we were ushered into their front room and the foster mam brought Donna downstairs.

What a little picture, what a beauty. Donna was a two-year-old with large brown hypnotic eyes but no smile to offer. She had mousy, shoulder-length hair that was allowed to just hang and she wore a blue pinafore dress. Donna would not come near me, but this was the first visit and after an hour we left and agreed to visit again the following evening.

On this next visit, Donna almost forgot her previous fear and immediately brought me one of her toys; she tilted her head and offered to me the slightest hint of a smile. That meant a great deal to me, it signified acceptance after such a short period.

Donna had been moved so many times in her short life that, in fact, she was too friendly towards strangers. She had known so many different homes that I'm sure, even though she was only two years of age, she probably realised that another move was imminent.

It had been agreed that the sooner Donna could move in with us then the sooner we could try and establish some bonding with her. I shall never forget collecting Donna and leaving that house with her and her meagre sole possessions crammed into a brown paper carrier bag. It was a beautiful summer Saturday afternoon and no sooner did we get home we thought that the more we can do to keep Donna occupied, the better as this was undoubtedly going to be a very difficult time for her.

However, she would be the focus of our attention and lunch was first on the agenda, followed by chocolate pudding. Now, every father must have a picture of one of their children having just devoured some type of messy food. This was no exception and Donna was covered from one end of her infectious smile to the other and that made a great photograph.

She enjoyed the afternoon and during the early evening she fell asleep on the couch but as she was placed into her new bed, soon awoke; her inconsolable tears were, from that time onwards, indelibly imprinted on my mind. She would cry herself to sleep every night thereafter for some considerable time.

Life was now about enjoying Donna and the pleasure she could bring to family life. Sadly, she was rather slow in her psychological development, the health visitor attributing all of her previous moves as a contributory factor. This lack of developmental progress was the last thing that concerned us as Donna was an absolute joy and made family life a reality, at least in those early years.

It seemed that life was, at last, becoming normal; however, in my experience, things just can't go that smoothly for too long and, sadly, this proved to be the case. I was devastated and concerned when I was unexpectedly taken poorly in 1984.

The night sweats had returned and there was a general deterioration in my health, which confined me to bed for around seven days. The emergency on-call doctor was summoned as I was getting worse and drifting in and out of consciousness. After his examination, he rang for an ambulance and I was admitted directly to Sunderland Royal Hospital late that night.

The following days were something of a blur, but one test followed another, something I was familiar with and although the working diagnosis was cancer - although I knew that I had no lumps or bumps, and after all of their exhaustive investigations, including scans and a lumbar puncture, it proved to be a significant viral infection. The huge problem with a cancer diagnosis is that you tend to assume that any cough, cold or other health problem must be a recurrence of the dreaded disease.

I do not believe that this was a paranoid tendency, it is an understandable reflex, a fear that cancer was again about to dominate my life and threaten my mortality. Thinking about it logically, of course, just because you have had cancer doesn't mean that you will not get anything else; of course, you can and you will, whether it's a simple cold to general aches and pains, it's simply about trying to rationalise and put everything into perspective.

As I have mentioned previously, the diagnosis of cancer doesn't just stop exerting its effects on an individual simply because the treatment has finished or even when a cure has been established. Earlier I described the strange effects of the chemotherapy drug called Vincristine and the effects it caused during delivery into my veins; the weird taste it initiated and the inexplicable sense of smell that hypnotised my senses into recalling an uncanny and nauseating sensation.

I would drink orange during its administration to try and diminish its effect but all to no avail. Well, some five years after completing my chemotherapy, which had proved a difficult time to say the least, I happened to be walking along a country path one day during the summer when the most nauseating smell filled my nostrils, the smell of Vincristine, making me feel physically sick.

But what was this unusual phenomenon and where was it coming from? It turned out that the smell came from a common countryside weed, called Rosebay Willow, also known as bomb weed or fireweed and, unfortunately, it litters the English countryside. Sadly for me, that smell was exactly like the drug that was administered into my fragile veins so long ago and strangely, I associated the smell with the unique taste of that drug Vincristine, and of course the nausea that accompanied the chemotherapy.

My inner senses were confused by this phenomenon, my psyche aggravated, my fears and darkest thoughts rekindled. There was bewilderment that I had not expected and the smell immediately provoked a physical sensation of nausea and the dreaded memory of what it was like to have chemotherapy. Today, I go out of my way to avoid any contact or proximity with fireweed as the strong association it has with the treatment I received. Proving, once touched by a cancer diagnosis, the reflection of its shadow is never far away, it is a lifelong legacy.

# Chapter 9
# The Words that All Parents Fear

In 1985, the year 'Live Aid' took place at Wembley and almost a year and a half since Donna, four years old, became an invaluable member of the family, things appeared to be going as they should or so I thought. It was a normal Saturday morning, plans for breakfast together and then a ride into town.

However, this particular morning turned out to be far from normal when I discovered a lump the size of a walnut on Donna's left elbow, which certainly hadn't been there previously. Naturally concerned, I hurriedly got myself and then Donna dressed and headed straight down to the doctor. Nothing to worry about, a simple infection in her arm, antibiotics will sort it out, was his response.

Donna was otherwise well and, therefore, I had no reason to doubt him, so I left the surgery, collected the antibiotics and then headed off home. Seven days later, having completed the treatment, the lump was still there, completely unchanged, so we went back to the doctors.

He sat in his chair and confidently stated, "*She simply hasn't responded to the antibiotics, we'll give her a different prescription.*"

He had examined Donna and found a small lump in her neck too, clear evidence in his view that this was an infection. Despite being dubious regarding his diagnosis, I had never had any problems with him previously and so I, again, accepted his explanation and headed off to the chemist to collect the next antibiotics.

Less than a week later, there was no change. This time, I took Donna straight to the Accident and Emergency department to see a Paediatrician, but even there the on-call doctor was quite dismissive of my concerns. As if to appease my nagging persistence, a blood test was taken and showed marginal anaemia and an elevation of her white cell count, which potentially could go hand in hand with an infection.

However, as far as the doctor was concerned, this was nothing to worry about. But, considering these findings, we were asked to make an appointment the following Monday in the children's ward in Sunderland Royal Hospital. I knew from my experience of illness that an elevated white count can be seen in several infective states but, of course, it could also be the first indication of something more sinister.

As such, I felt it warranted further investigation; particularly as Donna had already had antibiotics for fourteen days without any response. As requested, Donna attended the children's ward on Monday and had a variety of tests done during that week, including a biopsy of the lump on her arm that was causing so much of my concern. Despite all the investigations, she ran around the ward like an Olympic athlete.

The Consultant in his infinite wisdom decided that this was sufficient proof that Donna was a healthy fit child, seemingly basing his diagnosis on this fact alone as she was subsequently discharged home with no specific medical condition being detected. Instead, the Consultant declared that she would be as right as rain in no time.

Having no experience of health care apart from my illness, I felt ill-equipped to challenge his decision. So, I did exactly as he asked; I took Donna home, expecting her to resume normal activity. If the Consultant felt there was little to be concerned about, then who was I to question that expertise?

In the middle of the following week, whilst at work, I received a phone call from the hospital asking my wife and me to attend to discuss Donna's test results. I distinctly remember driving from Wallsend to Sunderland thinking it must be something serious, but never in my wildest dreams did I have any suspicion of what was about to be disclosed.

My wife had already made her way to the hospital and we met in the corridor and hurried along to the ward where the ward sister greeted us as if she had been expecting our arrival, directing us to two chairs placed regimentally outside the Consultant's office. During our wait, sitting there patiently, the dulcet tone of the Consultant could be heard asking the ward Sister to '*Get some tea and stay in whilst I speak to these parents*'.

This statement made me suspicious and I became concerned as to what he was about to tell us; my heart began to thump loudly and my mouth became dry as if stuffed full of cotton wool. My concern was well-founded as you could have knocked me over with a feather when the Consultant blurted out immediately we entered the room, without any compassion or hesitation, *"What do you know about Lymphoma."*

After a moment's pause, I responded, *"Are you saying Donna has Lymphoma?"*

His response was short and seemed to be lacking any empathy, *"Yes,"* he replied then marched out of the office.

This devastating news left us both numb with shock; the tingling pain of emotion was overwhelming, we were lost for words whilst our world was collapsing around us! It was so hard to comprehend and what angered me more than anything else was that, eventually, against all the odds, we now had the chance to share our lives with a bundle of joy, Donna and yet she was about to face the same life-threatening scenario that I had faced less than eight years earlier.

Her future was now uncertain; having to endure the same debilitating treatment I had received, the same treatment that had come close to destroying me not just physically, but also mentally. The main centre for paediatric Oncology was based in Newcastle and we were told to report to ward 16 South at the Royal Victoria Infirmary the following day.

We were so confused and upset when we arrived back home, not knowing whom to tell first or even if we should tell anyone at this early stage. We hoped that perhaps once we got to Newcastle, it would prove to be something much more innocent and not lymphoma, but was this just grasping at straws or would my hope be justified?

Remember, our family doctor told us that Donna had nothing more than an infection and the Consultant of Paediatrics told us that Donna was fine and too lively to be significantly poorly; we could only hope that both were right in that conclusion after all.

Donna had no symptoms apart from a few swollen lymph nodes and was indeed well I suppose deep down my understanding of lymphoma told me that these were not innocent swellings but, in reality, I wanted to avoid believing that and I had to have hope. We travelled to Newcastle the next morning, reaching the Royal Victoria Infirmary shortly after the rush hour.

We entered the hospital and made our way along what felt like an endless, green-tiled Victorian corridor, eventually, arriving at the oncology ward where we were greeted by the stench of antiseptic, which created a noticeable fear in the pit of my stomach. What's more, some children were lying on their beds;

others were running around the ward and many of them had no hair, a clear reminder as to why they were there and the treatment they had recently endured.

We were greeted by Liz, a young staff nurse, who became a good friend and confidante during the forthcoming weeks and months. There was little doubt that despite the seriousness of the conditions of the children here, the ward had a wonderful feeling to it, friendly and relaxed. Our first meeting with the Consultant compounded our heartache as a diagnosis for Donna was not as clear-cut as we had been led to believe and she would require further investigations.

Yes, she did indeed have a lymphoma; however, the specific type was unclear and clarity was essential as different lymphomas require different treatment approaches. One thing was certain; this was indeed a malignancy, a cancer, and a real threat to the life of our little girl. The biopsy had confirmed that diagnosis.

In those early days when blood was required and it was often daily, Donna simply offered her arm ready for the removal of the red substance, but it would not take too long before she learned that cooperation was not a requisite. She quickly learned that she did not have to give her consent freely or volunteer herself for tests that on the surface may appear innocent.

Donna very soon became suspicious of any member of staff who approached her and it became a battle, sometimes a psychological battle of persuasion, but at other times it would be a physical battle to retrieve the required samples or to persuade Donna to leave the ward for another test. Understandably, she could not comprehend the rationale for all or indeed any of these tests.

Whenever a nurse or doctor came to her bedside, she would compassionately look into my eyes as if seeking protection. My concern was that this situation would challenge our relationship; naturally, she was expecting me, her father, to stop these interventions from taking place but, clearly, I couldn't do that.

I was not aware at the time, but her cancer was in her bone marrow and the malignant cells were overcrowding this important space to such an extent that her healthy cells were unable to function or re-populate. Subsequently, Donna would require blood and platelet transfusions regularly.

One of the necessary tests was a repeated tissue biopsy, this time the enlarged lymph node in Donna's neck was to be excised and sent for analysis and it needed to be done in theatre under a general anaesthetic.

Now, anyone who has escorted his or her child to a theatre in readiness for an operation knows the fear and anxiety that runs through your body as you make the long journey down the busy corridor, the nurse running alongside the trolley trying her best to make Donna smile but failing miserably as she understood something quite unpleasant was about to happen.

After what seemed a half-marathon around the hospital, we finally arrived at the theatre and the fear really started to kick in. I had already been unable to convince myself that she was in safe hands and doubt entered my mind, a thousand confused fears suggesting to my unconscious mind that something may go wrong.

I felt overwhelmed by the silent screams trying to escape from inside my head, the pounding sound of each beat of my heart and the distinct dryness inside my mouth as I tried to put on a brave face for Donna as she held on tightly to lolly lodle, the name she had given to her favourite doll. All too soon it was time to let the anaesthetist do her job, but a gigantic lump stuck in my throat, a noxious sinking feeling consumed me when the theatre assistant suggested that we return to the ward once the fairy wind has taken effect and Donna had drifted into an artificial sleep.

Some hour and a half later and Donna was returned safely to the ward and slept for the next hour. Frustratingly, it was now time to play the waiting game, what exactly would the biopsy show? Not surprisingly, Donna made a full recovery from the theatre experience waking with an infectious smile, causing my tears to once again roll down my cheeks.

Sometime later that week, Donna was about to start some chemotherapy as a high-grade, Non-Hodgkin lymphoma had been diagnosed which required immediate treatment to prevent further advancement. The nightmare was about to commence, reliving and confronting my own fears concerning chemotherapy, I knew exactly what this chemotherapy was capable of and I worried about Donna's ability to cope with this difficult treatment.

My feelings of apprehension and emotional instability were matched only by the fear I felt watching Donna receive the chemotherapy drugs similar to those I'd received less than eight years previous. I struggled to accept the helplessness of seeing Donna undergo this chemotherapy and to deal with all the memories it elicited for me.

I felt completely useless, not being able to protect my little girl or have the treatment in her place. Indeed, it was harder watching Donna receive the treatment than it was to experience the similar, painful voyage myself and that had been an almighty struggle, yet I would have happily accepted the entire nightmare again if it would have relieved the need for Donna to be put through that torment.

Strangely and in many respects, Donna made life as easy as it could have been in that unenviable position, her smile and lovable character, her innocence and her trust in us as parents made that intolerable situation so much easier. If Donna coped, how could we as parents not? At times, it felt as if Donna was supporting us rather than the other way around.

From the very moment that you take your first tentative steps on the road of a cancer pathway, every day tends to merge into one and time is of little consequence anymore. The only thing that is of any importance is helping and supporting your child cope with what to them is an unknown experience.

You simply cannot explain to a three-year-old the full implications of a cancer diagnosis and particularly what the consequences of that diagnosis might be. That kaleidoscope of emotional turbulence returns and the roller-coast ride of unprecedented emotions firmly positions your sanity on the edge of time. Once on that roller coaster ride, it's difficult to stop the ride and get off.

It was all about to begin again, just as it did back in 1975, but this time I had far more understanding of the predicament and all of its implications, many of which I had simply not wanted to confront. However, this time there was no question of not being strong or not being able to cope, as I now had parental responsibility and an unswerving obligation to Donna.

Many discussions took place with both the medical and nursing fraternity, who had a wealth of experience in respect of helping parents address these extremely difficult situations. Many people may believe that a child has a right to know what is going on and attempts should be made to explain the meaning of a condition such as cancer.

However, many parents again will disagree and prefer to cushion their children from such exposure. Neither approach is correct, yet, neither is wrong. The correct choice has to be the one that is right for your child as you the parent see it. Once you make that decision, no one can criticise it.

As parents, we decided that we would explain to Donna as best we could about this dreaded condition, the most feared diagnosis known to society, a diagnosis that not everyone survives, although we wanted to avoid confronting that part of the brittle equation.

The mutual support from other parents we met at the hospital was incredible and it was a fact that you could not get through the nightmare without that support. Donna was fitted with a special device called a Hickman line that allowed the chemotherapy to be administered, blood to be taken and most importantly avoided the need for further needles to be stuck into her fragile veins.

The device has revolutionised modern-day chemotherapy, particularly for children. But even this marvellous device, didn't ease my feeling of helplessness at being unable to take away Donna's pain and sickness as only a father should. Donna soon lost her hair, but this really didn't bother her as much as it bothered us.

We found it offensive and hurtful when ignorant people would stand and blatantly stare when Donna walked past, clearly bald as a result of the unforgiving treatment; thankfully, she seemed unaware of their behaviour. Losing her hair was also a constant reminder to us of the seriousness of her current cancer and the threat to her life.

Donna was supplied with a brown wig and at every opportunity, she would proudly wear this. At times, however, when she was hot or eating something that needed her utmost concentration, it would be whipped off with a flick of her right wrist, often to the surprise of unsuspecting passers-by.

On one occasion between treatments, we had travelled to Blackpool, one of Donna's favourite destinations. During the visit, Donna had asked for candy floss and while she was eating this, the wind began to blow, causing hair from her wig to get in her mouth.

Undaunted, she simply put one hand on the top of her head and with one quick tug, the wig was removed and with impish nonchalance, she continued to devour the candy floss, the whole action having taken less than a couple of seconds. However, just at that moment, a gentleman was passing by and his bottom lip dropped almost to his feet as he observed Donna's actions.

As Hawkwind and the Lakota people had been such an inspiration to me, I couldn't but wonder if Hawkwind's music could help Donna? It turned out that she didn't like the majority of their music, but there were nights when Donna went to bed when I would sit at the bottom of her bed and play some of the more ambient Hawkwind tracks as she fell asleep, particularly a number called 'Wind of Change'.

Over the next couple of months, Donna got weaker and weaker and picked up one infection after another, which required many hospital admissions for intravenous antibiotics. Indeed, she had her fourth birthday in hospital. Donna was given some time off the treatment in an attempt to increase her weight and generally get stronger, but there was a need to weigh up the risk of breaking the treatment against the benefits of waiting to see if she improved.

However, after only two weeks, the team at Newcastle felt that it was important to recommence the chemotherapy as this cancer could not be left untreated. Sadly, following this treatment Donna appeared to suffer worse side effects than previously; a sickness that threatened to turn her stomach inside out and lethargy, leaving her bereft of motivation and an absence of her hypnotic smile.

With no desire to eat and incapable of moving from her bed, she was deteriorating in front of our eyes. There is no known coping strategy a parent can elicit when a child is struck by such an aggressive disease and, therefore, I cannot even attempt to explain how we as parents got through that impossible situation.

Make no mistake about it; the real coping mechanism was Donna! Despite her illness and suffering, she made things so much easier for us. Even though she was so poorly, Donna was a rock and made us feel very humble, as did all the children who were also with her on the same reluctant journey. With Donna so stoical, how on earth could we crumble in front of her?

Once at home, however, our emotions would fall to pieces like large chunks of ice falling from a glacier, my heart was breaking and at times I felt like an inconsolable wreck that could not see an end to this nightmare. Donna's mum suffered the same emotional turmoil and helplessness, in the same way, which I did. She too felt Donna's pain, yet together, we were unable to ease that suffering.

Yet as a parent, nothing but nothing can prepare you for the assault and battery inflicted by an unseen condition that affects every part of your person. But somewhere inside, you have just got to find the bravery and courage that is needed to support your child. Ultimately, you never lose sight of the determination, the focus that your child will get better.

Yes, there are times when you doubt that, but even then, you must convince yourself that one day the nightmare will end, if you don't, you'll lose your mind. On 22 August 1985, we were back in hospital at Newcastle for further treatment and things did not appear to be going to plan.

Donna was now so weak that I had to carry her from the car to the ward. The treatment itself was not having the desired effect against this vicious cancer and, therefore, further investigations were requested by Dr Craft, including a lumbar puncture. Donna appeared to be slipping away, losing her ability to live, her feeble frame now lying still on the bed, any movement causing her pain and upset.

Later in the evening, we were asked to go into the office with the Consultant.

It was obvious by his demeanour that this was serious, *"We do not think Donna can take any more chemotherapy,"* he said.

When I asked about the implication of this he said with heartfelt compassion, *"I'm afraid there is no more we can do for Donna."*

On hearing the words that each and every parent fears, the words you never want to hear, I have no shame in admitting that I just broke down and cried, my entire body numb with shock, my mind attacked by fear and no one able to take away that unrivalled heartache, no one able to ease this unbearable nightmare, my entire system tingling with shock and disbelief.

Not knowing what to do, what to say and how to react to an impossible situation. Eventually, as I sobbed, I recall asking Dr Craft the question that I didn't want an answer to, *"How long does she have?"*

That is a question that just cannot be answered with any accuracy, but what he said hit me like a brick wall in the face. *"She may go during the night, it could be days or weeks, she is so poorly at present."*

The feeling this news elicits is, undoubtedly, indescribable. Apparently, this was not a lymphoma after all. They now thought that what Donna had was an extremely rare form of adult cancer, called Chronic Myeloid Leukaemia and there was available treatment other than to keep her comfortable.

Donna was moved into a side room and we both stayed with her that night and it was an emotional tornado that I feared would never end. Donna was almost unresponsive in her consciousness, requiring lots of medication to keep her comfortable, yet despite my worst fears, Donna did survive that night and the next and the next.

The Consultant still felt that she would die soon and as a family, we were living on borrowed time. With such impending doom, I had to try to think logically. My little girl had been passed from pillar to post throughout her short life, known no consistency and according to the doctors, she was dying.

The main concern of my wife was that Donna had never been christened and even though the decision was not legally ours to make, we did exactly that and Donna was christened in the chapel at the Royal Victoria Infirmary. The Charge Nurse, Steve, was her Godfather and Liz, her named nurse, was her Godmother.

Afterwards, back on the ward, the staff had laid on a party for Donna and the other kids. That was a very unique day indeed and although Donna lay on her bed throughout the proceedings as she was so fragile, she still managed to smile as the other kids and parents all made the effort to ensure that Donna was the centre of attention.

The paradox of the situation wasn't lost on me; we were in the midst of a christening party for Donna, yet we were struggling to cope with the knowledge and persecution of the reality of losing our precious daughter. It remains the hardest concept to explain, you are told that your innocent child is going to die, yet as you watch her from a distance, it is impossible to believe, impossible to accept and even more impossible to understand.

How can you come to terms with this frightening dilemma? Quite simply, I do not believe you can. You can try to appease yourself that your child will be going to a better place if indeed you believe in a better place, but irrespective, there is still a considerable void, a chasm waiting to engulf the rest of your life.

You can try to put it out of your mind, but quite honestly we found that was almost impossible. Donna retained such a cheery disposition which made the whole process so surreal and strangely and ironically, it seemed that once again, Donna was actually supporting us, through that period.

No matter what your belief systems are, I do not believe any coping mechanisms can prepare you for the death of a child. With no treatment offered, the only plan was to keep Donna comfortable with blood and platelet transfusions whenever they were required.

This went on for almost ten days, after which time Donna was stronger than she had been in quite some weeks; strong enough to return home on the understanding that we brought her back each day for monitoring. The uncontrollable need and necessity to remain positive day in and day out in the hope that Donna would remain well became an exhausting occupation.

Talking with other parents in the same predicament as us, they would profess to be positive of mind, but admitted that it was hard work convincing oneself to remain positive. Within the seclusion and confines of your own home, time to reflect on the cancer that was engulfing your child and consuming your life that positive attitude would very often evaporate and seeds of doubt would often become an overpowering burden.

Interestingly, some months later completely unexpectedly, Donna spoke about the night she nearly died. She said she could clearly recall floating above her bed and seeing both her mum and dad crying and seeing a tunnel with the most unusual pretty bright lights at the end. She then claimed that a voice told her, '*It's not your time, go back to your mum and dad*'.

I'm sure many will pour scorn on this so-called out-of-body experience or this near-death experience, call it what you will. But this was from the mouth of a four-year-old and without any prompts. Even today, we know so little about life itself, especially the mind.

Of course, stories such as these are not uncommon but do lead to compound what is a complex, but fascinating issue. Whether this is the mind playing games, our inner psyche or something else is not open for debate here, but whatever it is, it is a fascinating discussion for another day. Little did we know that soon, we would receive the most unexpected news?

# Chapter 10
## Like Father, Like Daughter

Once Donna was back at home one of the first things that I would arrange, something I should have done months earlier was to start Donna on a daily dose of Ginseng. Was I grasping at straws? Almost certainly yes, but who knows what significance it played in my recovery, perhaps none, but it could have been one of a handful of significant ingredients in my successful recovery from my cancer diagnosis.

Irrespective of whether it had played any part in my recovery or not, what was important was that it certainly did no harm. Therefore, I went out and bought some Ginseng for Donna and she remained on the herb for many months, taking the elixir each morning without fail. Although it was harmless, it's not recommended to take it continuously, so she was given Ginseng for a month and then have a month's rest before starting again.

As Donna loved Blackpool, we planned to spend all of the time we had left with her going there as often as possible. Initially, following the terminal prognosis, we had decided to visit Disneyland in Florida, but we were advised against taking Donna out of the country because of her fragile condition and the risk of infection or the potential for her health to rapidly decline. Not to mention that medical insurance would not have been possible to secure.

Another worry was what I should do about work? I had been granted a leave of absence due to Donna's deterioration, but what about the longer term? As I felt I couldn't return to work with so much uncertainty surrounding Donna's very existence, I asked my employer if I could be granted voluntary redundancy, which they tentatively agreed to.

On reflection and I suppose in many respects, my request could have been seen as a knee jerk reaction because if Donna died, as predicted by the hospital, whilst that would be an emotional time, I would at some point, need to return to work. This dilemma added to my confusion as to what would be the correct course of action, but my focus at that time was to be free to spend as much time with Donna as possible.

Without a doubt, in a situation such as this, logic does not come into the equation and I guess that's why management insisted on taking a little time to consider my request. Less than a week later, my manager asked me to call into work at my earliest opportunity to discuss the request for redundancy.

He acknowledged the difficulty of the situation and offered to keep my job open indefinitely if I decided to continue to take a leave of absence. My mind, however, was made up; taking redundancy would give me the extra money I needed to do the things important to Donna and subsequently I took this option.

This, as far as I was concerned, would allow me to do what Donna wanted without the worry about finance. Once again, fate was playing a significant role in my life. Like so many others, Donna was a big wrestling fan. At the time Big Daddy (Shirley Crabtree) and Giant Haystacks were on the go.

Donna was a huge Big Daddy fan; so what a coincidence or was it fate, that when we drove into Blackpool, there it was emblazoned on a poster 'Professional Wrestling tonight', what's more guess who would be in the ring? Yes, none other than Big Daddy. How fortuitous and once settled into the hotel, my first job was to buy tickets for the show.

I decided to try and locate Big Daddies manager, which I did without much trouble and I explained why and how we were there and asked about the possibility of Donna meeting her hero. The manager said that would not be a problem and asked us to head to the corner of the hall after the show.

Big Daddy won the fight as expected and as we headed towards the corner of a now-empty hall as the manager had instructed; Big Daddy came out and invited us back to his changing room. He was an absolute diamond, superb, a true gentleman and, more importantly, he was fantastic with Donna, telling her that she was one of his heroes.

It was such a moment of emotion and there wasn't a dry eye in the house. Being aware that her life expectancy was limited and seeing her there with one of her heroes, it was wonderful to see her happy and content. As we made our way back to the hotel, that's all we heard about, Big Daddy, Big Daddy and more Big Daddy.

We returned to the North East the following day with Donna on a high and wearing her Big Daddy hat and scarf with pride. At the hospital, everyone was told about her special friend, Big Daddy and the nurses listened intently to Donna explaining how Big Daddy had beaten his arch-rival Giant Haystacks, her enthusiasm and pride at meeting this true gentleman was such a joy.

After the Consultant had examined Donna and taken the usual blood tests, she was given a platelet transfusion, other than this, the medical staff were pleased with her and there was no need for any further intervention. Therefore, after another day at home, we went to Blackpool again. It was almost as if Donna was a different girl compared to the young lady that lay helpless, weak and in constant discomfort only a few weeks earlier.

Occupying our minds with activities for Donna was not difficult and it was more than just a coping mechanism. Even so, the night before every hospital visit was a major concern, a mind-bending worry as to what would be said and what would be decided about her future? As the weeks went by, the visits to the hospital became less frequent and each time the Consultant was amazed at Donna's blood profile and he admitted to being completely baffled. More than a year later, the Consultant was bewildered as to Donna's recovery. Her blood counts were now normal and she remained in remission.

That'll do for me and long may it continue was my silent thought, I did not need explanations, as long as Donna was well was all that I could wish for. Naturally, the discipline of any child is an extremely important parental responsibility. Yet, try and instil discipline when the child is expected to die; it is just an impossible task.

Naturally, children soon realise that they can take advantage of a situation if they do not get told that they are doing wrong and that's exactly what happened with Donna. On the majority of occasions discipline was none existent if she misbehaved herself, so now was the time to put a halt to that mistake.

Even poorly children need to know wrong from right, although it is a difficult transition once you have ignored misdemeanours for so long. Between trips to Blackpool Donna was sent to London by the charity, Dreams Come True. However, it wasn't just a trip to London; Donna had loved Jason Donovan for many years and at that moment in time, he was playing the lead role in Joseph and the Technicolor Dream Coat.

Therefore, she not only got the opportunity to see the show but also to meet Jason afterwards. The weeks, with dozens of trips to Blackpool, turned into months as Donna became physically stronger than she had ever been, although she remained susceptible to infection, her immune system still fragile from the consequences of chemotherapy.

Yet, by their admission, the Oncologist and Haematologist were both bemused at Donna's recovery, neither of them had any answers to this inexplicable recovery. It was at this time that Donna had a desire to go to school. Her friends had started some weeks earlier, but we had been advised not to allow Donna to start her education as she remained immunocompromised.

However, how on earth could we deny her this wish? Therefore, we discussed it with the hospital and they decided that it would probably be a good idea and one way of getting her back into some semblance of normality. And so we planned for her to start school.

Donna was all kitted out for her first day at school and she certainly looked a picture that inaugural day, although her hair was only just beginning to grow. My greatest concern was the ridicule that she may have to endure due to the style of her hair or the fact that she was educationally slow.

We all know how cruel children can be, especially to each other and, therefore, I had great unease and a sense of nausea in the pit of my stomach as I led her away from home towards the school. That first trek was, without a doubt, a poignant journey. For Donna though, it was a wonderful day, a new and exciting time of her life.

In the playground, as the whistle blew, the lump in my throat refused to disappear as I tried in vain to put on a brave face as Donna turned to me, waved and smiled as she entered the doors for the first time. At least twice during that day, I had deliberately walked past the school in the desperate hope that I would catch sight of my vulnerable little girl.

My fears proved unfounded as she came home that afternoon euphoric with stories of newfound friends and the work that she had done. Thankfully, the teachers had already discussed with Donna's classmates, explaining to some degree how poorly Donna was and how she needed support from them all.

During the first year, the majority of children did exactly that; support her, although sadly there were a few exceptions. The school was good for Donna, at least for the initial year. After this time it was evident that Donna was not only struggling with the work but also with some of the other children who, at times, would tease and taunt her.

Children can be so cruel and in many respects that is almost understandable, but much to my disgust, one of the teachers was highlighting the fact that Donna was different from the other kids and would emphasise this by making Donna sit at the front of the class, on the floor and facing the blackboard.

Donna was very upset about this and, apparently, it had been going on for some time before one of the other children had mentioned this situation to me when she was playing with Donna. I was not about to let this one go! I demanded a meeting with both the head teacher and this individual to ask for some explanation, how on earth could this person call themselves a teacher?

Furthermore, I demanded that it stop with immediate effect and although the head teacher appeared weak and hesitant, he took steps to ensure that it stopped forthwith. It was obvious that something had to be done about this predicament and, as her parents; we would have been failing Donna had we not taken this action.

Now everyone knows children can be very cruel, but Donna's teacher's actions seemed to be an instruction to some of the children that Donna could be teased and ridiculed. This bullying, call it what you will, was not going to go away. Aside from the mental anguish, we had noticed that Donna's speech, as well as her reading and writing skills, appeared to be behind other children of a similar age.

Subsequently, as parents, we felt her education was being affected and this should be investigated further. The headmaster wanted Donna to continue as she was but as her father, I did not feel that this was acting in Donna's best interest and, therefore, I contacted the educational psychology department for an official assessment and it proved to be the right move.

The assessment demonstrated that Donna had a mild deficit in her cognitive ability and had specific educational needs, a learning disability. Learning disabilities are seen in children who have epilepsy, kids who have had cancer in the first five years of life and also some adoption studies have demonstrated that learning disability is possible following adoption or fostering.

But irrespective of the cause, this deficit could not be addressed by mainstream education and subsequently, she was placed in a school for children with both physical and mental difficulties. At this educational establishment, Barbara Priestman School in Sunderland there was a great rapport between the children and the teachers.

Regarding her leukaemia, in 1990 when Donna went for her six monthly follow up, she saw not one, not two but three Consultants. Donna greeted them with her infectious smile, yet not one of them could explain Donna's incredible

119

recovery. Subsequently, Donna was discharged from further follow up and declared to be cured. Some things in life, you do not need an explanation, for me, this was one of those times!

Generally, Donna's time at this school was a happy one and, significantly, it was a school that encouraged the personal development of something inherent in each child. The philosophy was that each child had something they were good at. When questioned, Donna expressed a keen interest in swimming and a desire to improve the basic skills she already had.

Her choice was brilliant and would certainly reap rewards for her in the not too distant future. Following all of the chemotherapy she had received, Donna had developed epilepsy that by the admission of all of the experts would prove very difficult to control with conventional antiepileptic medication.

Indeed, for almost three years Donna was having hundreds of mini-seizures daily. Drug after drug had failed to have an impact on her seizure activity. Remember, Donna had chosen to improve her swimming prowess, not something that usually goes hand in hand with epilepsy. However, contrary to popular belief, it is safe for epileptics to swim, providing they have a recognised spotter on the poolside, essentially someone who knows what to do in an emergency situation.

So, it proved that Donna would become more than just an average swimmer. The school did everything it could to encourage and promote Donna's skills. I enrolled Donna in a local swimming club to help develop her technique and to her credit; Donna worked exceptionally hard at her swimming and became quite adept. It also improved her self-confidence.

She comfortably achieved dozens of certificates and despite her cognitive deficits; she could swim for miles and miles. Donna certainly had belief in her abilities regarding swimming.

Every year, Donna's school would take part in a regional swimming event at Darlington's Dolphin Centre. This competition was a variety of swimming events that for the successful individual could lead to bigger and better things, national events, including consideration for the England swim team.

At this event, Donna had been entered into no fewer than six different races and her nerves were obvious, but I told her that this was all about concentrating on her ability and forgetting all about her disability. Each of us is good at something, it's just a matter of finding exactly what that potential is and then honing it, if you think you can do it, you can do it!

As the time drew closer and closer for her first competitive race, it was patently clear that Donna was physically shaking and doubt crept into her mind. As she stood on the side of the pool awaiting the starting gun, I marched up and down the poolside nervous and concerned, my stomach in knots and I hoped she would remember everything about reacting to the gun and getting a good start as she had been taught.

'Take your marks' and then, BANG! Donna flew through the air like a bullet and streamlined into the water similar to a dolphin, immediately taking a short lead. Halfway up the first length Donna suddenly went under the water and floundered. What seemed like minutes was in fact only seconds but I was flabbergasted that none of the lifeguard's had gone in to rescue Donna as she was having an epileptic seizure in the pool.

Naturally, they had been informed before the event that she was an epileptic and had given her the go-ahead to compete, so whilst they hesitated, I ran along the poolside and without a second thought dove fully clothed into the pool to rescue Donna. Meanwhile, at exactly the same time, Steve, Donna's swimming instructor from school had also realised that nothing was being done and he also dove into the pool.

Donna was quickly pulled to the side and recovered fully from the incident. I will not highlight here what I said to the lifeguards but I'm sure you can guess. It didn't end there though. What is so amazing is that once recovered from the seizure, Donna insisted on continuing to compete in the remaining five races.

However, even more amazing, she incredibly won three silvers and two gold medals that day. What an achievement! But that was just the beginning of her swimming adventure. On the bus home, the other school children congratulated Donna but had a good laugh at Mr Russell and myself and our unexpected swim.

Donna had now tasted competitive success and for the first time in her life realised that she could do something particularly well, she quickly learned that she excelled at swimming. So, a new episode of adventure was about to take off.

Donna was excited and was determined to train longer and harder to achieve her dream. With her allowance, she would search out the very best equipment that afforded her the best opportunity for success and despite her educational deficit; she would also become very knowledgeable concerning qualifying times for different competitions and events.

Donna became a regular at the Darlington swimming event and won dozens of medals over the years. On one occasion she was greeted by Tony Blair when he attended the gala to support the competitors. He later became Prime Minister so that was a story she often told.

Donna became a regular in the local press too and received much favourable recognition and awards for her swimming prowess. Naturally, when she came up against able-bodied club swimmers she didn't fare as well, although she could hold her own, yet this never demoralised her and simply proved an additional motivation.

In 1995 Donna was invited to Rugby to try out for the England swimming team. The English Sports Association for People with Learning Disability was an excellent opportunity for Donna to receive top class instruction from nationally recognised swimming instructors and also the chance of representing her country.

After her trial, the head coach said she would like Donna to attend the next training day. From then on Donna was a regular in the England training camp, although it would be a little while before she got into the actual team for an official event.

The other individuals were very supportive of one another and the team would meet up approximately every three months, a time which Donna looked forward to. A few years later Donna was invited to take part in the Danish Open Swimming Championships in Copenhagen representing England. That was a very proud moment and I accompanied her there.

She returned with only one medal, but lots of experience and, in many respects, the medals were secondary and I always told Donna that no one could ask any more of her other than her best, if you give your best and don't achieve a medal, this should not be viewed as a failure, far from it.

Donna's swimming was improving beyond recognition and she very much wanted to join an able-bodied swimming club that could take her to the next dimension, one that would push her to her limits. Therefore, having done some investigation, I got Donna into Chester-Le-Street swimming club and this would prove an excellent move.

Although specific competitions would prove few and far between from an international perspective, Donna would remain an active member of the English Sports Association for People with Learning Difficulties and the England team for many years. We would travel all around the country to different venues and different competitions collecting a whole host of trophies and medals. She also made lots and lots of friends.

That same year, Newcastle United played Manchester United at St. James Park, and I was among the capacity crowd that saw the mighty magpies dominate the red devils from start to finish, running out five to nil winners.

The legendary Alan Shearer was awarded the Premier League player of the month award, for September, 1998, and generously dedicated this prestigious award to the English Sports Association for People with Learning Disability. More importantly, Donna was chosen to go along to St. James Park to accept the award on behalf of the Association. Naturally, I went along too.

Later in 1996, Donna was nominated for a MacDonald's child of achievement award in recognition of her swimming achievements following her recovery from leukaemia. She travelled to London to meet stars from both sports and media at a gala event. She was presented with her award by Right Honourable John Major, at that time, Prime Minister.

This seemed a million miles from the heartache of only eleven years earlier when her precious life appeared to be slipping away. However, in 1998, the incredible happened; Donna was approached by the head coach of the Great Britain Para Olympic team.

He had been monitoring Donna's times for specific events and she had amazingly dragged herself into the reckoning for a place in the Great Britain team due to fly out to New Zealand for the World Swimming Championships in Christchurch. The final place was between Donna and another young girl and after much deliberation, Donna got the news she had been dreaming of, the final place in the team was hers.

I was very proud, to say the least, the day her Great Britain tracksuit arrived by post and she modelled the attire that evening. In the next couple of months before she was due to leave England on that long journey to New Zealand, Donna worked so very hard at training and even the local television station arrived to feature her build-up to the Championships.

The day arrived when Donna was due to meet up with the rest of the Great Britain team at London's Heathrow Airport. Donna and I set out early that morning to London by train and I remember that at Durham train station, a businessman came up to Donna and said he'd seen her on television a couple of nights earlier and wished her all the luck for the forthcoming competition.

I was so proud; I felt like seven feet tall, while Donna just stood there and smiled. Even though I could not journey to New Zealand with Donna, I was kept informed by telephone of her progress in every swim. She swam in the heats of the 50 meters breaststroke, her favourite stroke and managed to make the final.

The following day the final was scheduled to take place, with eight swimmers in total, Donna would not only need a personal best in the event, but she would also need to sprout wings as she had the slowest time of all the swimmers. Importantly, just getting into the final was a credible achievement in itself, but even more, was to come.

In the final, Donna did swim a personal best and finished sixth overall, a fantastic feat. A few days later Donna was picked to swim in both the 4 x 100 meters and 4 x 50 meters freestyle relay. These races proved to be very competitive, yet the Great Britain girls' team managed second place in both events and, subsequently, Donna came home with two silver medals from the 1998 World Swimming Championships.

I was the proudest dad in the world and made it my business to tell everyone of Donna's achievement. I couldn't wait to see Donna on her return from New Zealand and set about arranging a surprise party as a celebration with friends and relatives. Donna was now at the top of her game and enjoying her swimming more than ever before.

Some months later and a national event took place at Reading; naturally Donna would enter a handful of races. However, importantly, it was the successful relay team that would once again take the limelight during that event. On this occasion, not only did they win the event, but they also smashed the world record at that time.

As difficult as it is for me to admit, Donna's younger sister suffered as a result of Donna's previous ill health and the demands that Donna would have concerning her cognitive deficit. Admittedly, as a parent, I think there were times when due to the worry and fragility of Donna's illness that it became an overwhelming everyday concern that was totally consuming.

Even during her recovery and the fear of relapse, her sister did not receive the parenting she was entitled to and, in many respects, it's too late to put that anomaly right. This is perhaps my greatest regret in life and, unfortunately, there is no way I can go back and undo that and it remains my burden to live with.

# Chapter 11
# My Belated Education

During the time that Donna had commenced her swimming career, life was, at last, returning to normal and it was now that I had an important decision to make, a decision that would affect the rest of my life. Having accepted redundancy from my previous employment, it was now time to return to employment. The big question was what would I do?

The answer was never in any doubt—nursing! I had developed a great respect and admiration for those who had nursed, encouraged and cajoled me through the real prospect of an early and premature death. I admired and respected the nurses who had more than just nursed Donna through a life-limiting disease; they had psychologically supported the whole family.

Unfortunately, I had no qualifications to gain entry into the nursing profession therefore I decided to return to full-time education for twelve months to gain the requisite qualifications that would allow me a new direction in life. Returning to education after being away so long, to a system that I had treated as a joke, proved difficult for me and I had to work especially hard to ensure I did not fall behind in my studies, yet perversely it was enjoyable.

I had taken five GCSEs and one 'A' level during that academic year. I could have stretched this over two years, but I wanted so desperately to begin my nursing career that I was determined to do it in one year. Despite having gained the necessary grades, getting into nursing would prove more difficult than I had anticipated.

I was interviewed by three different nursing schools, Newcastle, Sunderland and Gateshead. During the interviews, when asked why I wanted to enter nursing, I was completely honest about my cancer history and also my future aspirations within the Health Service. Unfortunately, even this far down the line even the Health Service can demonstrate negativity and prejudice concerning an understanding of cancer survivorship.

Both Newcastle and Sunderland were impressed with my foresight and determination to make nursing a successful career and offered me a place there and then. Sadly Gateshead, which was my first choice of venue to train, felt that because of my background, they could not offer me a student place.

Taking a place at Gateshead would hopefully have allowed me to gain employment in my home town hospital, South Shields; the hospital which fourteen years earlier had made my cancer diagnosis.

Although disappointed, the belligerence of these nursing leaders left me confused but I was content to ignore their obstinacy and accept a training place at Newcastle. My immediate aim was to qualify and then work on ward 38 at Newcastle General, where I had received much of my treatment and then one day return to my native South Shields to work in my home town hospital and give something back to the local community, specifically in cancer care.

In May 1989 I commenced nurse training with pride and expectation. The training was hard work but very enjoyable and I was fortunate to train with a great group of student nurses, almost all females and I had the unenviable distinction of being the oldest student in the group and jokingly they never let me forget that!

After an initial six weeks in the classroom, we were all allocated to a ward to spend ten weeks gaining knowledge and experience of the nursing profession, but that was only the beginning as nurse training would take three years. My first ward was a surgical ward and I could not wait to start.

However, I would soon have the enthusiastic wind knocked out of my sails. The ward was a busy unit dealing mostly with abdominal surgery, much of which was for malignant disease. In the first few days, I looked after a little old chap, who appreciated a chat as much as the direct nursing care required for his condition.

Clearly, my friendly approach wasn't appreciated by everyone as the ward sister insisted that I met with her in her office and, once in there, she immediately laid the law down telling me that I was getting too friendly with the patients. She insisted that I was there to learn and not to befriend the patients.

I was more than taken aback and thought that she was pushing nursing back into the dark ages. Surely communication was identified as a fundamental aspect of care, so was it necessary to distance ourselves from the patient? I didn't think so, but I was just a student nurse and didn't voice my opinions. Keen to be the best nurse I could, I accepted her rebuke, although deep down, I knew she was wrong.

I think in many respects her approach spurred me on to hopefully be a good nurse. Throughout my nursing career, I met lots of nurses with varying degrees of aptitude and caring. I particularly remember the way some of the qualified staff would speak to and treat student nurses, without respect, care or compassion.

I concluded that if they could treat student nurses with such contempt then what was their actual patient care like? It was those early days that made me determined not to follow the paths of those with a negative and dictatorial approach to their care, they were not good role models. Admittedly, some nurses do the profession a great disservice, but the vast majority are enthusiastic and dedicated to the cause.

I placed a lot of endeavours on my theoretical work too as it was important to be able to underpin the practical skills with cognitive ability. My first piece of work was on Hodgkin Lymphoma and mostly came from my own established knowledge and was reflected in the lecturer's comments, '*An obvious understanding and empathy of this condition*'.

My pride endorsed the fact that this was the right career for me and even in those early days it was a pleasure and a privilege to be influencing the health of people dependent upon nurses and doctors in the health service. Even for those individuals who were terminally ill, to be part of a team that could improve their symptoms and makes their dying days peaceful and pain-free was worth more than any salary could ever achieve.

In my second year of nurse training, I got the opportunity to spend a ten-week placement in ward 38. I did wonder how I would feel nursing patients in the very same environment where I was, myself a patient fourteen years previous. However, my fear and apprehension were unfounded and it proved to be a very happy ward to work on.

All of the staff knew of my previous illness and were, without exception fully supportive of me and all the other student nurses allocated to the ward. One of the Auxiliary nurses, Pat, was an Auxiliary when I was a patient and naturally we would reminisce about the years gone by. Being a nurse was a massive and steep learning curve and having worked in a shipyard previously, this was at the complete opposite end of the spectrum.

Still, my mind was made up and my goal was to attain a job as a staff nurse on ward 38 once I qualified. That would prove to be my motivation throughout some of the more difficult times. During my time in ward 38, I once again met up with the two Consultants who had previously treated my lymphoma.

Indeed, I would often accompany them on ward rounds. It was undoubtedly, a weird and perhaps unprecedented relationship. For the previous fourteen years these gentlemen, I had known only as a patient. Now, they are colleagues, discussing and advising me on the management of their cancer patients entrusted into my care.

There were even specific times when the sister of the ward would approach me and ask if she could tell certain patients about my story and, naturally, I never declined this request if it was to be of benefit to other individuals. On those occasions, patients would often ask about the differences in treatment and how as an individual I coped with the sentence of a cancer diagnosis.

Clearly, a diagnosis of cancer still brings with it an unprecedented fear but even in this honoured situation, it would have been wrong of me to say, '*I know what you are going through,*' because quite frankly, I didn't. Everyone's cancer journey is unique, as is a patient's individual experience.

Working in the stressful environment of cancer care causes many different kinds of pressures, pressures that need to be released and nurses are certainly well renowned for going out and enjoying themselves, it's called a release mechanism. There were numerous times throughout my training and beyond that I would be invited out.

Most often I felt that I had to decline these social occasions as my wife at the time would create merry hell and make all kinds of ridiculous accusations and insinuations such was her jealousy. Therefore, instead of allowing these situations to arise, I would simply make any excuse not to attend and even on the few occasions that I did go out with various teams from different wards, I felt obliged to take my wife along; at least it saved me from getting too much grief on my return home.

During nurse training, I was allocated to a variety of different wards that would give me the maximum amount of experience. I spent ten weeks in one of the paediatric wards and that gave a whole new dimension to nursing. It was not just the children who needed care; the parents required psychological support and that presented a different challenge to your nursing skills.

Naturally, during each placement, the student nurse would be allocated a mentor, someone to supervise and support the student and to assess the skills you were to achieve on that placement. During those ten weeks, a difficult but enjoyable and educative placement, I spent most of my time caring for a small boy aged two and I got to know his parents very well.

His condition was uncontrollable epilepsy brought on by a condition that resulted in his skull being misshapen and which also affected his brain. The child had spent most of his life in hospital in a vain attempt to control his epilepsy and this reminded me very much of Donna.

Some six weeks into my placement, the Neurologist's were considering whether brain surgery would help improve his condition and the decision was a very difficult one to take, both for the surgeons and his parents such were the risks involved in the procedure.

It was at this time that I made what I now consider to be a bad decision; I decided to ask if I could be present if and when the boy went to the theatre. Having reviewed the situation, the Neurologist decided to take the youngster to theatre and operate on his brain. The parents, although understandably very anxious and concerned about the procedure, said that they felt a little better because I was going to be in the theatre with him.

Things went well in the first couple of hours and went according to plan. Sadly, things quickly deteriorated as the child began to experience problems and, sadly, he subsequently died in theatre. This was the most harrowing experience of my student days so far and not what I was expecting.

How on earth could I now face the parents, as they had such confidence in me being in the theatre with their little boy?

The Consultant Neurologist knew that I had a good rapport with the parents and asked if I would accompany him to break the tragic news to them. I certainly did not feel as though I could refuse his request, but this was not something I had been trained for and neither was I prepared for such a situation.

The parents were waiting immediately outside the theatre and before we even spoke a word they knew things had not gone to plan. How can you try and console parents in that situation? There are simply no correct things to say and this was no exception, you cannot make that dreadful situation any easier for a parent.

I struggled to maintain my composure such was the extent of their unbearable distress. In fact, strangely, they still felt comforted by the fact that I'd been in theatre at the same time that their little boy had died. Once back on the ward I was inconsolable, one of my colleagues on the same ward as me tried in vain to comfort me but to no avail.

Life indeed was so cruel. Where's the justification, the reasoning for the loss of an innocent life being needlessly wasted? To this day, I keep a photograph of the youngster at home. Life as a student nurse was extremely difficult, but also very enjoyable, throwing up many new and unexpected challenges.

Hand in hand with the difficult situations that I would face on the wards, there were also the exams and coursework that needed to be submitted by specific deadlines. At last, during my third year, I got the opportunity to return to ward 38 and this proved to be my future motivation.

I knew within the first few hours of working on ward 38 during my final year, that once qualified, there was no other discipline I wanted to work in other than Oncology caring for individuals with different cancers and what's more, I wanted to continue to work on ward 38.

I felt that I had the passion and the empathy but also the dedication to deliver what is undoubtedly a difficult and unpredictable job, dealing with cancer patients and all of the physical and psychological problems they have. In addition, I contended that it would also allow me to give something back in return for all the care and dedication I had received during my illness.

I had another two ward placements to go, yet I knew neither of these would match up to the satisfaction of dealing with cancer patients. Looking after patients receiving both chemotherapy and radiotherapy but also those in the terminal stages of their disease was the most satisfying occupation I had known.

I finished my penultimate placement and had only one more placement before the final examinations that would hopefully qualify me as a staff nurse, provided I passed the exams of course. The last ward placement was intended to consolidate my management experience and could have been anywhere.

I now had a cunning plan, if I went to see the allocation officer and tell her a little of my history and also my desire to work in Oncology, perhaps she would be sympathetic and give me my last placement on ward 38. So, I did exactly that and low and behold, the allocation officer was more than supportive.

Subsequently, I had my last student placement on ward 38 and not only did this fulfil my needs, but the staff there were superb. Irrespective of my bias towards Oncology, they were a first-class group of nurses and in hindsight an excellent team delivering a high standard of care. At the end of the ten weeks on ward 38, I prepared myself for the final weeks in class and then, the final examination.

I was not good in exam situations but I wanted this qualification very badly. Everyone was full of their last placement and also their trepidations regarding the forthcoming final exams. All of my preparations were complete, I knew that I could study no more and that it was now down to me, no one could do this for me.

However, I had studied hard over the course of the three years and I was quietly confident. Days before the exams I got word that a junior staff nurse post would be coming up on ward 38 soon after the make or break exams and needless to say, I would eagerly await the advertisement for that post. The finals could not have gone any better; there was even a question about cancer management which was ideal for me.

However, like all exam situations, I initially came out of the exam full of confidence, but then began to slowly sow my own seeds of doubt as I reminded myself as to the additional information that I thought I should have included. It would be weeks before the results were posted, what a wait, what anxiety, what doubts, but, I also had hope and an insatiable appetite to succeed in my nursing career.

In the interim, the post on ward 38 was advertised and I immediately rang personnel for an application form. It arrived two days later and I completed it immediately. Meanwhile, back in the classroom, we were given presentations in respect of interview techniques. One or two of my student nurse colleagues had already been interviewed for jobs and a few had been fortunate to secure positions.

Eventually, the day came when the results of the exams were due. I was up first thing in the morning drinking cups of coffee until I was buzzing. And there was the postman, swinging the gate open and walking carefree along the path, unaware of the important documents he had in his possession. He pushed a bunch of letters through the letterbox and I quickly rummaged through the pile until I found the one I wanted.

I ripped it open to read: 'I am pleased to tell you—Yes, I had done it; I had passed those all-important exams, I felt such relief and joy. From being diagnosed with cancer more than seventeen years earlier to having my life turned upside down and inside out with the devastating diagnosis of Donna's illness I was now in the privileged position of being a qualified nurse determined to gain a future in cancer nursing.

Ten days later a letter arrived which provides an added impetus to my thrust for a job, I had an interview for the post on ward 38. On the day of the interview, I was as high as a kite. Sitting outside the interview room my heart was thumping so loudly that it was probably putting the other candidates off.

Then, when it was my turn to be interviewed, as I stood my legs turned to jelly and I wasn't sure if I could walk through the door. The interview panel were sitting there smiling and making it as easy as they possibly could. The questions started and I felt as if my tongue was covered with cotton wool, but eventually, I got my answers out.

It seemed as though I was in there for hours before they released me from this important interrogation and they promised to ring me later that same day. For the remainder of the day, I couldn't concentrate on anything. One hour merged into the next before the phone finally rang with a voice I immediately recognised; the Sister from ward 38.

She starts to tell me that I did very well in the interview and while I was pleased to hear that all I was thinking, just get to the point. However, when she said, '*We would like to offer you the post on ward 38,*' all thoughts went out of my head and for once in my life, I was absolutely speechless, yet I managed to mumble something to her that probably made little sense.

I don't mind admitting that later that night a bottle of 'Jim Beam' was almost emptied in celebration. And so, things were eventually going as they should do and I could look forward to a new career as a staff nurse, working on a cancer ward, but not just any cancer ward; ward 38 where I had been so well supported, not just by other patients but also the staff. Cancer survivorship was surely a virtue.

# Chapter 12
# Climbing the Ladder

Nursing on ward 38 was interesting and rewarding but very demanding and stressful and, yet, I spent a very memorable seven and a half years there, learning a significant amount that would stand me in good stead as my cancer nursing career accelerated.

The nursing team were excellent, made up of different characters that complimented and supported one another and also knew the importance of humour. Not only was it important that I consolidated my nurse training and gained some valuable experience, but it was also important that I got the necessary educational additives that nursing demands.

During the first few months as a newly qualified staff nurse, I went back to college one day each week and completed a teaching certificate. Teaching would prove an important component of my practice over the forthcoming years and it remained so throughout my nursing career.

I do believe teaching is integral to the nursing profession and that we must share the knowledge we have learned, no one has the exclusive right to information, sharing knowledge and experience is one of the major ways to improve patient care. Of course, what I do have is my experience and knowledge as a patient and yes, I can share my stories, but that is still not the same as the cancer experience.

It is, I believe, my best asset and the one that has enhanced my nursing practice more than any other attribute. Mentorship is an important component of the nurse's armament, it allows the qualified nurse to pass on their expertise and knowledge to student nurses and, equally, it allows the student to shadow the qualified nurse and learn from their tutelage.

I believe that the knowledge I have accumulated does not belong to me alone, it has been gleaned from a variety of sources and therefore, I should share it with others. During those very early days, one of the most important conversations I had with a student nurse was something that was influenced by my experience not as a staff nurse, but as a cancer patient.

A student nurse who incidentally was very enthusiastic and determined to learn said to me during a busy early morning shift, *"Aren't cancer patients happy and well-adjusted, they cope very well?"*

Now, this statement stuck in my mind and served as a good example of the stereotypical attitude of many individuals, students and qualified nurses alike. My response on this occasion was, *"Remember, we only see these patient's when they are on the ward we do not see them when they are at home."*

I think this is a critical point; nurses can go off-duty at the end of a shift, forgetting all about cancer care until the next day. In contrast, cancer patients do not have the opportunity to go off-duty; they are permanently on duty, regardless of where they are or what time of the day it is. Often, the perception the cancer patient portrays is a brave face, coping with all that life throws at them and able to cope and carry on with life normally. But how true is this perception?

I would perhaps argue that in the main, this is a false illusion, not because they deliberately want to deceive health care professionals, it's simply that we do not realise the difficulties the cancer patient faces when away from the safety and security of a dedicated health care environment. On another occasion, one of my patients, an elderly lady with terminal cancer, was talking about the times she enjoyed during her childhood.

She began telling me that one of her favourite pastimes when she was a child, was doing cartwheels for the benefit of her disabled brother. It was then that I got the bright idea of demonstrating my prowess at performing cartwheels and proceeded to do exactly that along the corridor, much to her delight.

Unfortunately, it was precisely at this time that the departmental manager came onto the ward and demanded that I stop this stupidity and go directly to her office. Red-faced, I made my way to her office and was given a verbal lecture. I felt that I could justify my actions as there were no obstacles in my way and importantly it had given so much pleasure to this lady who was dying; it had done no harm that I could see.

Sadly, the nurse manager didn't quite see or understand my rationale and I was instructed that this idiotic behaviour should stop forthwith. Only three days later, the lady for whom I had performed my acrobatics sadly died; however, the patient in the opposite bed told me that the lady had told her family with great fondness about my show and how she truly appreciated it.

Twelve months later, I completed my teaching certificate and I was keen to continue with further education, but it had to be something that would have an impact on patient care. So, I applied for a scholarship that would allow me to spend some time at Birmingham University to undertake a certificate in clinical hypnotherapy.

Again, hypnotherapy would prove not only a considerable benefit to my clinical practice but also to my nursing career as a whole. Hypnotherapy remains an undervalued therapeutic tool that can not only enhance the cancer patient's well-being; it can also alleviate many of the debilitating side effects of treatment or indeed the symptoms of the dreaded disease.

On completion of the certificate in Clinical Hypnotherapy, I became one of only a handful of nurses practising hypnotherapy in the health service in the UK at that time, an accomplishment I was immensely proud of. Over the forthcoming years, many patients would benefit from this complementary therapy that I was now using to great effect.

As early as 1994, research suggested that more than 70% of cancer patients had considered the use of complementary therapy at some point during their illness. Of course, all forms of complementary therapy can be used alongside traditional treatment but not in place; they should not be seen as alternatives.

On an almost daily basis, cancer patients present the health care professionals with new challenges but, even so, it remains a pleasure and a privilege to be doing this work. Working at Newcastle, I was still seeing Dr Bozzino or Dr Atkinson on an annual basis for check-ups, but I also saw both regularly in a professional capacity.

At my next appointment, Dr Bozzino decided to discharge me from his follow-up clinics on the strict understanding that should I have any concerns, then I immediately contact him, from a patient's perspective, although he did not expect that I should need to. Much to my concern, some eighteen months after my discharge, I would indeed require his help again. I had begun to experience searing and unexpected pains in my head.

Without warning and at any time of the day or night, it was like someone was inserting a red-hot needle into my skull. The pain was only momentary, but it was also excruciating and, therefore, fearing the worst, I contacted Dr Bozzino as he had suggested. He wasn't quite sure what the problem was but indicated that a malignant relapse could not be ruled out and arranged an emergency brain CT scan.

He had insisted that this examination be carried out sooner rather than later, yet the week's wait seemed like months and was accompanied by many sleepless nights and moments when I imagined being told that my cancer had reared its ugly head once again. To make matters worse, I kept all of this to myself, denying myself any support from family, friends and colleagues.

How would I cope with a relapse of my disease? It was so far away from what I had anticipated was a complete cure. Many confusing thoughts went through my mind over those seven days and I do not mind confessing that I was terrified as to what the cause of these painful headaches could be.

It was obvious what my greatest fear was but if it did prove to be a return of the lymphoma, or even a different cancer, what would my response be as I was well aware of the psychological struggle I had experienced years earlier. The legacy of cancer survivorship was certainly not straightforward!

The closer the day came to have the CT scan, the more I convinced myself that this indeed was a recurrence. Eventually, the scan was undertaken and thankfully, my fears proved unfounded and the scan showed no evidence of malignancy. There must have been a reason for this debilitating pain and as this was not a condition that Dr Bozzino could address, he referred me to a neurologist.

Later in the month, I saw a neurologist who explained that what I was suffering from was a form of migraine, called 'Ice pick' headaches. These were closely linked to stress and anxiety and I certainly had plenty of that at home. Still, I was relieved that this was nothing more sinister. Perhaps with the explanation of a cause, these 'Ice pick' headaches would settle down.

At work, I had recently completed the Oncology course, a significantly important qualification aimed specifically at nurses looking after patients with cancer. Soon afterwards, I was offered the opportunity to work as a higher grade staff nurse covering ward 37, which looked after predominantly female cancer patients.

This would be for a period of six months and the experience was supposed to stand me in good stead for the prospect of operating as a higher grade staff nurse when one became available on ward 38. After eighteen months of working in Oncology, I was as happy as a sand boy, doing meaningful and fulfilling work and I felt ready for a higher grade permanently.

My colleagues agreed and encouraged me to apply for the next available post, but it would take a further eight months and three interviews later before I eventually secured a higher position. It never fails to amaze me the way that fate works. During the morning of a very busy shift on ward 38 I was met from the elevator by the feeble figure of a young man, his face pale and engraved with fear, I'd seen that fear in the mirror before.

Beads of sweat stood to attention across his forehead as he introduced himself in a nervous voice as *Simon (*name changed). Unfortunately, such was the busy state of the ward that Friday morning that I couldn't attend to him immediately and had to usher him into the day room along with his brother and girlfriend, promising to return to them as soon as I could.

Less than five minutes later, I was summoned from the drug's trolley by Simon's brother. Understandably concerned and knowing how important it was that Simon started some chemotherapy for his disease, a Mediastinal Teratoma, he explained that Simon had decided that he was going to return home and forget about the chemotherapy treatment.

Naturally, this situation took priority and I managed to find someone to take over the drug round, so I could attend to Simon. I took Simon, his brother and his pregnant girlfriend into the quiet room, the same room that I had occupied with Syd many years earlier. I knew this situation only too well, but did not feel that I was out of my depth.

However, I could not just go in there and blurt out that I had also had cancer and knew what Simon was going through. Firstly, I did not have the faintest idea what was going through his mind and secondly, I was going to be led by Simon.

Given the privacy in this quiet area, Simon told me that he had heard so much about chemotherapy and knew he could not face the prospect of the treatment's side effects. Simon was very close to tears and barely managed to keep these back and I have to admit I was quite emotional during that difficult encounter.

Simon acknowledged that his fears were founded around the horrendous stories of treatment that are often portrayed by the media generally. Such stories only serve to terrify future patients, leading them to expect or anticipate side effects that are not necessarily going to occur. My explanations of the potential side effects and stressing that these were indeed potential, served to get our relationship off the ground.

Despite still being a novice staff nurse with not a great deal of counselling experience, I took a monumental decision, rightly or wrongly, to share some of my experiences with Simon; particularly my fears and concerns about treatment. Simon and I soon discovered that we had much more in common than a cancer diagnosis, not least; we both came from South Shields.

Furthermore, we shared a passion for rock music and Newcastle United Football Club and we both enjoyed horse racing—the sport of kings, although neither of us was very successful. According to Simon, he was about to undertake the most frightening ordeal of his thirty-two-year existence—the commencement of chemotherapy for his cancer.

I had embarked on that very same fearful and traumatic journey over eighteen years earlier and this was to be our unique bond. It seemed that fate had played such a strange game with my life. Uncertainty and fear as a young man sitting in that quiet room aware that my life expectancy may be short, to now sitting here fulfilled and proud that I appeared to be helping someone in their battle against the physical and psychological onslaught of their cancer diagnosis.

For every procedure from now on, Simon would seek my thoughts and experiences on that particular matter. The medical and nursing staff became aware of our unique rapport and supported the situation. Importantly, it needs to be pointed out that it is not my practice to tell all patients about my diagnosis and treatment experiences. But, in this instance with Simon, I knew instinctively, that it was the right thing to do and so it proved to be the case.

Simon encountered many problems on his first admission, mainly recurrent infections that proved difficult to control and caused him to have an extended stay in hospital. Ironically, he suffered very few side effects from the chemotherapy treatment. Sadly, however, over a period of some seven months in and out of the hospital, he had set back after set back and control of his disease was never fully attained.

Infection followed infection and a bone marrow investigation revealed extensive infiltration, signifying progressive cancer. Simon and his girlfriend were spoken to by the Consultant and the Macmillan nurse and told of the fateful results. Simon was told face to face that he would not recover from this cancer.

Strangely, although his girlfriend was understandably devastated, her eternal optimism now shattered, Simon appeared relieved and said that he always knew this would happen. Simon died at home only a few weeks later, surrounded by the people who loved him. Clearly a sorrowful situation, yet I have no hesitation in identifying this incident as a positive one and worthy of inclusion in this chronicle.

Yes, despite modern-day advances in cancer care, Simon did die. But, on so many occasions, he imparted to me how important our relationship was to him. Furthermore, at a time when, as a staff nurse, I was still consolidating my nurse training, this positive incident has had a great impact on my clinical practice and I feel it has moulded my practice today.

A few weeks after Simon's death, I received the most fantastic letter from the family thanking me for the input in Simon's management. What greater thanks could there be? There is, however, something from this situation that I call survivor guilt—despite my support and care for Simon and his loved ones, the fact that he died and I was still alive, made me feel strangely guilty, a bizarre emotion that I would experience many times over the years to follow.

So, why do nurses working in the discipline of cancer services do what they do? Simply, because they are compassionate and committed because they want to make a difference, they accept that it is a privilege to be involved with these patient's, yet by the very nature of the disease, the fact is many patients will lose their battle making this a stressful and difficult job; leading nurses to confront their own mortality.

In my view, just because someone has a piece of paper, representing a diploma or a degree, does not mean that they are any better at doing the job than the person who does not have that equivalent qualification, I sometimes think that far too much emphasis these days is given to those pieces of parchment; it could also be argued that it attracts the wrong kind of a person into the profession, a person who might see nursing as an access route to a degree.

Of course, education is vital so that we can continue to grow and mature cognitively but nurses caring for cancer patient's need empathy, commitment and, above all, good communication skills to make a difference for the simple reason that if we fail then so do our cancer patients. We would also fail the patient's family and that negative experience can leave a permanent psychological scar that is difficult to overcome and detracts from their quality of life. This makes employing the right people into cancer services as fundamental.

Approximately six years after qualifying, I felt that it was now the time to broaden my horizons. It had always been my ultimate desire to work at South Tyneside, where my original diagnosis had been made. The opportunity to move on from ward 38 into more senior positions was almost non-existent, but I was ready to try.

Naturally, I was cautious as to moving on, I had such a unique relationship with ward 38, first as a patient, then as a staff nurse and part of a very successful and happy team and it proved to be a considerable wrench leaving the ward. Of course, it wouldn't be straightforward, as I would need substantially more and broader experience than I had.

Therefore, after much deliberation, I decided to apply for a post as Charge Nurse in a busy chemotherapy day unit at Sunderland Royal Hospital.

Unknown to me, one of my colleagues from ward 38 had also applied for the same position. Admittedly, she had more experience than I had and also had a degree and although I was working towards mine, I did not actually have it. We were both offered an interview along with other nurses from other hospitals.

I remember giving a superb interview and being told that the candidates would be informed of the outcome the following day. Both *Lucy (*name changed) and I were on duty the following day and it was around mid-morning when I took a phone call from the personnel officer at Sunderland. She asked to speak to Lucy, which I thought meant only one thing, that she was being offered the job and this proved to be correct.

Thirty minutes later the phone rang again, this time the personnel officer wanted to speak with me and told me that I had not been successful. Without hesitation, I congratulated Lucy, but understandably, deep down I was disappointed. However, this was the first senior post that I had applied for outside of Newcastle General Hospital and I knew there would be other opportunities.

As a believer in fate, I accepted the situation, yet only seven days later Lucy decided that her career would take a different direction and she rang Sunderland Royal Hospital and retracted her acceptance of the senior position. When she had told me this my feelings were a little subdued, I knew the post would now be offered to someone else, but if it was offered to me, would I accept being used as second best and would I want such a position having been overlooked in the first instance?

That all-important telephone call came, offering me the post. I asked for the weekend to consider this and promised to call back on Monday. After much deliberation and soul-searching, I decided that this was too much of an opportunity to decline. In addition, it was a significant stepping-stone towards my ultimate aim and I accepted this very prestigious and senior position.

Managing a department and group of staff was a significantly different proposition than anything I had previously undertaken. Visiting the chemotherapy day unit at Sunderland Royal Hospital to introduce myself was important. It was a relatively small team and all were well experienced in the administration of chemotherapy.

In fact, I knew some of the team already. Paula, having undertaken my teaching certificate with her some six years earlier and June, whom I had met many years earlier when she had lived close by during Donna's illness. Donna had played with her little girl, Emma. I was keen to start this exciting new role and test my skills in management; but as always, I aspired to significantly influence patient care.

During my three years in post and after many patient satisfaction surveys, positive feedback from senior management and colleagues and most of all, the comments given from patients and carers, I do feel I achieved that goal. Throughout all of my years of employment and socialising, I had never had such a good friend and confidante as I did with June.

From day one of my becoming manager of the Chemotherapy Unit, we hit it off, we got on so well together that almost immediately other nurses started making suggestions that we were romantically involved, as only nurses can! Nothing could have been further from the truth, we were perceptive friends, we knew when either of us had a problem and needed to talk.

I had already confided in my sister Allyson, a full twelve years earlier, that my marriage was not working, that I was unhappy. However, for the sake of the children, there was never a question of leaving so early in the lives of my young girls. They were completely innocent in the equation and in addition, they both deserved some stability in their lives, at least until they were old enough to understand, although perhaps they would never understand.

However, I did not tell my wife how unhappy I was in the marriage, to do so would have been a huge mistake and would have made life intolerable for both the girls and me. I would decide to dissolve the marriage when Donna and her sister were old enough to acknowledge and understand that sometimes, two people are just incompatible and have to go their separate ways.

My intention and desire to break up the marriage at the time that I did was filled with naivety. I had hoped that my wife and I would remain friends following the break-up, particularly for the good of the girls, but sadly, this would be an impossible wish to attain and I was foolish in making that assumption.

The marriage had hit an irretrievable point, arguments were becoming a daily occurrence, no one could deny that and often for no meaningful reason. But there was so much more than just arguments. It was a difficult situation because the children were the innocent victims in this no-win situation.

It was a very exciting and enjoyable time regarding work, but also a very difficult one as my marriage was clearly in the throes of failure and although I had attempted to keep this from my work colleagues and indeed my children, the latter had been aware of the domestic friction for some time. Donna was now eighteen and I had to give serious consideration to my future and the direction it should take.

Work was a great distraction, of course and June's friendship at that time was invaluable. However, despite the circumstances of my marriage and the cruel rumours circulating, there was no romance between June and me at that time, but there was certainly something drawing us together. Perhaps the entity of fate was once again working here?

Divorce proceedings would prove hostile and aggressive and naturally, the children found the entire process very difficult, neither wanting to take sides, at least initially. Further than this, I want to avoid being perceived as being vitriolic; therefore, no more will be said of that. Thankfully, my friends and family were very supportive and aided my difficult journey through the marriage break up.

Soon after, I decided that I needed a new challenge and direction in my nursing career and subsequently began searching for another job. Not long after this decision, a position arose as a Chemotherapy nurse specialist working for a private company in the community. Was this the answer I was looking for?

I was interviewed for the post and subsequently offered a position with the company, but in retrospect, after only a few months, I would deduce that this was not the right move for me, particularly in the early days when the other chemotherapy nurses were still very inexperienced, the onus of responsibility was placed with me as the most experienced practitioner.

Not only did I feel misled and without clinical support, but I found some of the practices unacceptable, occasionally bordering on dangerous. However, staying there for a few years did broaden my experience and eventually, the arrival of Lucy (*name changed) would dramatically improve my feelings about the post.

I had worked with Lucy at Newcastle some years earlier and she was a great asset and extremely knowledgeable, perhaps one of the most knowledgeable nurses I have worked with. Despite my initial reservations, this role would subsequently lead to my ultimate dream and, therefore, I would again be thankful for my fate.

There is little doubt that at that time June would continue to be my best friend, our common bond, outside of nursing, was the break-up of our respective marriages and yet we had so much more than that; she was there when I needed a shoulder to cry upon and always ready to offer some rationale and pragmatic advice, despite her worries and troubles.

I can't say when and I can't say how, but at some point, the close relationship changed from one of friendship to one of intimacy and romance, it was and remains the best thing that had happened to me in a long, long time. Love is the finest thing known to man and yet, in many instances it is spontaneous.

June and I were no different and without a word being said between us, we fell in love and our relationship went from strength to strength. I think it is fair to say that we complemented each other to such a degree that she knew my thoughts and I knew hers; at long last, I had found my true soul mate.

After the break-up of my marriage, I lived with my mam and after almost ten-month, I wanted to get a place of my own again, but finding somewhere suitable would not be easy. I actually had no problems living with my mam, as I had a fantastic relationship with both my parents, but it was time to move on.

Once again, fate would play its role. I had seen a seven bedroomed house for sale at a very reasonable price and although I didn't need that number of bedrooms, I had to give it a viewing. The owner had decided to offer open viewing and along I went. Naturally, June came too.

However, entering the house, it was plain to see that this enormous property was an excellent price, but it required significant work. In addition and probably more importantly, it did not have a comfortable feel and I, subsequently, dismissed it from my options.

However, when leaving that house, June noticed that the dwelling next door was also on the market, a similar Victorian building with vacant possession. I noted the estate agent details and decided to call the next day. It turned out that the house had been empty for almost twelve months, once again; fate had intervened in my life.

Again, I took June and, this time, her nine-year-old daughter, Sophie, with me to view the potential home. The house had real character, built-in 1875 and it had a comforting feel to it, despite clearly needing a lot of work. Instinctively,

I decided immediately that this was the house for me and the following day I put in an offer, which after some months of deliberation was accepted.

Every single room needed work, but this was also an investment. Some months later, lock, stock and barrel we moved in, although the work to update the house would continue for many years. September 1999, the time when Sir Bobby Robson became manager of my beloved Newcastle United, we were now comfortable in our home despite it being a work in progress.

During our first Christmas together I proposed to June, she had little hesitation with her response and thankfully it was yes. Not long after setting up home together, we had unexpected housemates; firstly Emma, June's eldest daughter needed a roof over her head and then Donna split from her boyfriend and had no one to turn to, nor anywhere to go and, therefore, her first choice was that of her dad.

Without hesitation, quite naturally, she too moved in with June and me. There is little doubt, that at times things were difficult, but we never doubted our resolve or relationship, which remained solid.

Eventually, Emma would move in with her boyfriend and sometime later would present us with a beautiful granddaughter, Courtney, my princess. It didn't stop there, either. Donna to set up home with her boyfriend, although much to my dismay, this would be in London; however, my only concern was that she was happy.

Amazingly and despite her previous treatment, Donna would present us with a Grandson, Kieran. This is what life is all about, grandchildren, we shared so many happy times and over the years, Courtney would even share my passion for Hawkwind and Newcastle United, joining me as a season ticket holder.

From an employment perspective, my dream came true in 2001 when an advert appeared for a Haematology Clinical Nurse Specialist at South Tyneside Hospital. There was little doubt that I would apply for this prestigious post, this was what I had yearned for. But, it's the same with every job application, you submit the completed form along with your summary of experience and then sit back and wait for the post.

I was confident about getting an interview, but not so confident about getting the job, as there was sure to be other well-qualified and experienced nurses applying. A couple of weeks later and the postman delivered the letter I was waiting for, telling me of my interview date and the presentation I would be expected to deliver before the interview itself.

For the next couple of weeks, my head was inside my books, brushing up on the current legislation regarding haematology. Thankfully, it all paid dividends, following the interview the telephone call I dreamed of came, the job was mine. No sooner had I been told, I rang June at work to tell her the good news; next, I telephoned my manager Lucy, who knew about my ambitions and explained that I would be tendering my notice and she too was pleased for me.

I couldn't wait to take up my new post, a post that I believe I was destined to fill. The legacy of survivorship had now led me right back to my hometown hospital, the same hospital that had made my diagnosis some twenty-six years earlier; if that is not fate, then I do not know what is.

Since then, it has been a pleasure and a privilege to provide haematology nursing care at South Tyneside District General Hospital. My role involved many aspects of care, including dedicated clinics, often breaking bad news diagnoses to patients and relatives.

The strange thing about this situation is that we use the very rooms where I, all those years earlier, received an abundance of chemotherapy, where I was told on more than one occasion that the treatment had failed and the exact room where the junior doctor had attempted and failed to retrieve a bone marrow sample from my feeble chest.

Ironically, as the haematology nurse specialist, one of my functions was to perform all bone marrow investigations. It is a strange entity of fate, you cannot predict it, you can certainly tempt it, but I believe you cannot change it. Working in the field of Haematology and dealing with individuals afflicted by the same cancers that both Donna and I had is strange.

How does it make me feel? Most definitely humbled and honoured, but strangely, at times, haunted by survivor guilt. I felt guilty that I had survived when I had to acknowledge that not everyone does survive this feared disease. Most of all though always respectful that I am in that position and influencing people's lives and hopefully making a positive difference in their quality of life, only they can answer that, but what I do know is that my practice is heavily influenced by both Donna's and my own illness experiences.

In 2004, legislation called 'Agenda for Change' was introduced. This meant all nurses had to justify their roles and complete job descriptions. It also meant that this would determine your individual pay grade. Eventually, I was awarded a band 8, (the highest banded cancer nurse at South Tyneside) and the additional title of 'Head of Haematology Services'. Fate had taken my pride to a new level of accomplishment.

Doing the job that I do, I inevitably see many people lose their battle against cancer and that is very sad and very often difficult to accept. If I had a pound for every patient that I had helped to care for, I'd be a rich man. Yet, paradoxically I am a very rich man, not financially but rich in the fact that I have and will continue to play a part in the care of so many wonderful people, each one touching me differently.

Forget about prizes and rewards in the health service, what better accolade can a nurse receive than the thanks and praise of the people they care for? It's all about patient satisfaction. It would certainly be impossible to mention all the individuals with whom I have had the privilege to be involved with. I could easily fill a book with stories of courage and conviction from the many patients I have had the honour to nurse and be part of their care.

So many fantastic people, not only the many brave individuals who have fought with dignity and pride against an illness that would ultimately claim their lives, but also those who continue in their fight against the most indiscriminate of conditions. I salute you all and thank each and every one of you for my participation in your care, I remember you all and I hope I made a difference.

What about when someone dies? We have two choices, either we can close our eyes and continue to be sad or we can open our eyes and remember them with fondness and recall the happy memories we have of them. I say that with sincerity and honesty and hope that it does not insult anyone, as it is certainly not intended to.

Cancer nursing forces you to look at life differently. Sometimes, inspirations just happen and I'm no different. At the age of forty-seven, I had this sudden urge and desire to learn to ride a motorbike. In all of my years, I had been on the back of a bike twice but never ridden one, yet I now had this need to fulfil another dream. June was a little apprehensive, but if that was what I wanted, then she gave me her unconditional support.

Subsequently, I contacted a local training school, did the required basic training, followed by the requisite written exam and then went on to do my full riding exam which I passed on the second attempt. Now I needed a bike! But not just any bike, it had to have some credibility. Subsequently, I bought myself a Daelim Daystar, a copy of the early Harley Indian; which, I felt, would do for a few years until I got more and more experience, after which time the objective was, of course, a Harley.

For those who have not experienced it, there is no better feeling than riding along the coast road, the wind blowing across your face with the open road ahead. Freedom and pure escapism rolled into one, a great rush. For many years, I rode a Suzuki Marauder 800cc and sadly, I never did get my Harley, although I still live in hope.

Extremely content at work, time rolled on for June and me. Our years together have been good and admittedly, there have been some difficult times to deal with, but never with our relationship; it remained and still is solid, rock-solid and hand on heart, I can honestly say that we have never had crossed words.

On more than just an isolated occasion, June would ask, '*When are you going to marry me,*' to which I would most often reply with flippancy, '*At some point.*' I had proposed in 1999, so why was I always so flippant? Well, it had always been my intention to organise the wedding and then surprise her with a specific date.

I had already agreed with Terry to be my best man, checked with important members of the family that they would be available to share this magic moment and so, in 2003 I booked the town hall for the following year, 29 August 2004 to be precise. Rather than surprise June in a restaurant with a ring, an approach I knew she would not appreciate.

I, therefore, had to think of an alternative idea. So, when she suggested that we stayed in for my birthday, I thought this was an ideal opportunity, with much of the wedding booked, to repeat my proposal. A candlelit evening, good food and a nice bottle of wine to enhance a wonderful occasion, I gave her a card with an invitation to her own wedding, including all the arrangements and for once in her life June was speechless.

Needless to say, she accepted. That was a great night and will remain firmly embedded in our fond memories forever. That was a particularly poignant moment for me too, why? Well, I had arranged the wedding including the afternoon reception at a local Spanish 'Tapas' restaurant and a night-time celebration at 'The Sea Hotel', I now told June that all she had to do was choose the music that she wanted to walk down the aisle too.

June was startled at this request and felt strongly that she did not want to be walking down the aisle and suggested that I walk down instead. Jokingly, I retorted that if I walked down the aisle, then it would be to the sound of Hawkwind; astonishingly, June simply said, *"That's fine."*

I began to think maybe this wasn't such a bad idea anyway, as Hawkwind had been part of my support network through some pretty bad times over the years, so why shouldn't they support me during the good times; at my wedding.

As far as I was concerned, given the influence it had on my life, I could not think of any more fitting music than that of Hawkwind. Who knows, without the support I found from their music, I may not even have been here to see this day. Subsequently, we agreed that June would sit at the front of the chambers with the guests and Terry and I would walk the aisle preceded by Courtney to the space rock music of Hawkwind.

The months ahead were filled with organising and arranging what would be a glorious occasion. On the day, the hall was filled with our guests ready and waiting, not for the bride but the groom, his best man and the flower girl.

At precisely 1.00 p.m. the registrar asked for quiet and then the gentle sound of 'World of Tiers' from Hawkwind's Levitation album was played as Terry and I stepped confidently down the aisle with Courtney proudly leading the way. We had planned and written much of the service ourselves and I proudly read it out on behalf of both of us and in the presence of our friends and family.

As part of the ceremony and as the indigenous people of the North American plains had also played a considerable part in my illness, another of our friends, Davey, read out a Native American wedding blessing.

Wedding vows confirmed we walked together down the aisle to another Hawkwind track, this time, the softer ambient number 'Lost Chronicles' from the Xenon Codex album. This certainly was proving to be a day to remember, although it wasn't over yet. At the reception and as tradition dictates, Terry read several wedding cards before he started his speech, but he saved one card until last.

This final card he read out was, to me anyway, the best of all; it was a congratulations card from none other than the members of Hawkwind, signed by each one of them. This was proving to be one of the best days of my life, it was important to me that Hawkwind had shared my wedding day, as well as my illness.

June has always been fully aware of the fact that Hawkwind was and remain an important component in my life and she had no hesitation in supporting my desire to share this special day with the band. Our night-time party was wonderful and a simple continuation of a brilliant celebration that will remain firmly embedded into the conscious and unconscious thoughts of us both forever.

June is aware of the importance of the Lakota people in my life. The support they offered, without taking anything in return. The solace I took from their history and their spirituality, without them even knowing this fact, is something I could never repay. She would, in years to come, share an experience of the Lakota Oglala people and their important history.

However, I feel that because of what had gone before, I never really knew who John Walker Pattison was. But, in 1999, I began to realise the man that I had always been.

# Chapter 13
# My World Falls Apart

I'm not unique and neither am I special, many others have experienced the devastation that is cancer and undoubtedly many more will do so in the future. A cancer diagnosis changes your life, it is a permanent attribute; it is with you wherever you go and during whatever life throws at you and although you learn to cope with it, it's just impossible to cast it the shadow aside.

Even though you may not think about it every solitary day, no matter what you do, it is always in the back of your mind and therefore never far away. People who have had a cancer diagnosis learn to live with the most feared label that society knows. The experience will forever change your perception and personal philosophy.

It is only now that policymakers in government and health care are starting to acknowledge that survivorship requires support - long-term support. Survivorship brings with it many new challenges and health-related issues. For many decades, survivorship meant coping alone; this new approach to providing long term support is a welcome change in attitudes and policy.

No scholar can define in a textbook the seriousness of a cancer diagnosis and all that it brings unless of course they have been touched personally. Healthcare professionals can certainly demonstrate empathy, but they can only try to understand the true potency of cancer and its ability to corrupt an individual's sanity, influence emotions, manipulate the mind and elicit the greatest fear known to man. In my view, it remains a life-changing experience of unparalleled equivalence.

Next to heart disease cancer is the biggest single killer in the world today and we are still no nearer an overall cure although significant improvements have been made concerning treatments and survival rates. Cancer is a word synonymous with fear and also sadly stigma and as the statistics tell us we all have a 1 in 2 chance of being given a cancer diagnosis at some point in our lives; yet despite those statistics, there is very little information about how to deal with it psychologically.

Today, Hodgkin lymphoma is now most often associated with a cure but make no mistake, Hodgkin lymphoma still claims lives.

As more and more individuals survive cancer we are starting to be able to piece together its long term effects. Whilst cancer survivors living thirty, forty years and more following treatment remain in the minority, more and more individuals will attain that target in the coming years, allowing us to determine what the long term effects of treatment truly are.

Better detection of the disease and also more sophisticated investigations and improved drugs aimed at targeting cancer cells more specifically have helped improve the survival data for many cancers. There is still a need to look at ways of supporting long-term survivors of society's most feared illness. The cancer jigsaw is complex and many pieces are still missing from the puzzle. We need all of those pieces before we can begin to see the whole picture.

The published data in respect of developing cancer as a result of the treatment (Carcinogenesis) is rather ambiguous. Some data dismisses the risk while others claim that the risk is as small as 5% to as much as 40% depending on so many variables, including the type of cancer you had in the first instance, the type of treatment, age gender and much, much more.

Research demonstrates that lymphoma patients, in particular, have a higher risk of developing a secondary malignancy or leukaemia due to previous treatment.

As a survivor of cancer for more than forty-seven years I was unaware of that risk, so it wasn't something I had to consider when deciding to receive treatment, although neither was I asked to consent to treatment. However, I know that patients today are given so much more information than ever before, and legally, are required to sign a consent form in order to commence treatment.

Health care professionals are legally obligated to explain the short-term and long-term risks of treatment. Individuals also have much more information to hand and may question whether undertaking difficult treatment is worth the risk of secondary malignancy and chronic illness. No one other than the patient can answer that question, but only if they have all of the information they require.

In retrospect, as a patient, had I had this information many decades earlier, would I have gone ahead with the very treatment that I struggled to tolerate for so long? People may say, 'If I had cancer, I would do this or that'. To those people and with respect, I say, until you are faced with that very situation you just do not know how you're going to react.

I discovered the risks and literature in respect of secondary cancer as a result of my nursing career. At first, it hit me full in the face, as if I'd been hit by a centurion tank. For weeks I never slept and was uneasy with my discovery. So many questions streamed into my mind at the most inopportune moments, but the most important question was what could I do about it?

Not a lot unfortunately other than to be aware of my own body and report anything of significance to the doctor and undertake a healthy lifestyle as far as is possible. I believe that all relevant information needs to be given to cancer patients before they start treatment so that they and they alone can make an informed choice about treatment.

Having the information about health-related morbidity upfront would also help cancer patient's deal with the issue, not only in the longer term but also as survivors. One could question if it is right to burden someone with this kind of information as they already have sufficient to deal with in the first instance and how many people might refuse the opportunity to be cured because of the potential risk of developing a secondary cancer, or chronic illness many years later, if at all?

So what is the right answer with regards to whether patients about to commence treatment for cancer should be told of the risks with respect to long-term side effects of chemotherapy? It seems contradictory to the process of patient empowerment and informed consent to deny patients this knowledge; do they not have the right to make the decision that is right for them? After all, the information is available on the internet, so it is far better being explained by a health care professional.

Had I been given this information and then decided not to accept chemotherapy as a treatment modality, one thing is for certain, I would not be here now relaying my journey to you. Certainly, the ethical dilemma of the long term consequences of the treatment will continue.

In my view, it is an additional burden cancer survivors must shoulder and although it is easy to say, it is a burden that must not be dwelt upon, although that is easier said than done. Importantly, although research can identify the longer-term health-related side effects, it cannot agree or define the specific risk of developing another cancer as a consequence of the primary treatment.

Today, this risk is likely to be lessened due to the fact we now use more targeted therapies, such as drugs that are aimed at specific cell surface antigens, immunotherapy and CAR T therapy (Chimeric Antigen Receptor T-Cell). Radiotherapy is much more of a targeted treatment than it was in the 1970s, which led to some of my chronic illnesses. Needless to say, more treatments will be developed in the coming decades.

It is not my intention to scare or worry cancer survivors, surviving survivorship is hard enough but I raise the issue primarily from a patient's perspective. It is a fact that all of this information is readily available on that wonderful medium we know as the internet; the media have also been known to print articles on the very subject from time to time, but not always accurately.

As a duty of care, I feel the health professional has an obligation to tell cancer patients about these risks to ensure that they get the facts rather than the fiction. The media are responsible for much of the scaremongering in respect of cancer. All too often we see patients portrayed in a negative light, experiencing horrendous side-effects of treatment, particularly when seen on television.

Side effects these days are less severe and better controlled than a decade earlier. However, that is certainly not to say they do not occur that would be a foolhardy statement, of course, they do but the lesser side effects do not diminish from the seriousness of the disease or the harsh reality of chemotherapy.

The problem with negative portrayal is that it can cause permanent damage in the minds of the patients and their loved ones, heartache and unnecessary grief for those currently undergoing treatment. For those diagnosed with cancer and about to embark upon its treatment pathway, there is an expectation that those side effects, often graphically highlighted will definitely occur, instilling fear and trepidation into the very minds of individuals about to receive the treatment.

In my view this cannot be right, surely the media can appreciate that accurate reporting is not only their responsibility but also imperative to cancer patients. I'm not saying that they should not report on public interest stories such as cancer; I'm simply asking that they report it with diligence and an understanding of the need for clarity.

They never report on the thousands of patients who have chemotherapy and continue to work and the thousands of patients who today have the treatment and do not experience side effects. However, these commonplace stories do not sell newspapers or make for good television viewing and therefore we seldom see these in the media.

Sadly, the media prefer to fuel the fear of society regarding malignant disease by simply endorsing the stigma that has become known as cancer. The media also need to remember that cancer is not automatically a 'death sentence'. Today, the prognosis for many cancers is better than at any other time and advances are continuing faster than journals are printed.

New and improved drugs to help combat the unwanted side effects of treatment are now available and very effective, however, we should never ever underestimate the psychological scarring that is caused by a cancer diagnosis. We should all, the media included, acknowledge and address this psychological damage and recognise that survivorship is a specific health-related issue.

Similarly, when new chemotherapy drugs are discovered, they should be reported with scientific awareness. Often the headlines proclaim a cure or new treatments for specific cancers. When these stories are examined in-depth, the reporting is often way off target and wholly inaccurate.

This in itself gives false hope to patients with the specific cancers cited in their features and serves to demoralise individuals when they attend the hospital to discuss these treatments only to be told that either they are not suitable for their cancer or the drug mentioned is still in the trial phase and not actually available as a treatment at that time.

Whilst the media do have an obligation to report new developments in cancer care they also have an obligation to report them correctly. No one can imagine, myself included, how it would feel if it had been reported that a new wonder drug had been developed, only to be informed at the hospital that this was not the case. We see this in clinical practice frequently.

We cannot play mind games with cancer patients, their state of mind is often very fragile and such behaviour could cause further psychological trauma. In the same context, fertility issues raise a variety of concerns for cancer patients undergoing treatment. We know which drugs cause infertility, so there is a need to be careful with the selection of the drugs used for treatments, but also, individuals about to undergo chemotherapy need to be informed of the fertility risks.

Sperm banking was never an option for me back in 1975, but as the small number of longer-term survivors increase we are learning that men can have a regeneration of their sperm, sometimes twenty plus years later.

It was the build-up to Christmas, 1999 the highest and lowest point in my entire life came within weeks of each other.

June had been feeling slightly under the weather over the previous few weeks, she had a suspicion as to what the cause was, but then, she had convinced herself that her suspicion was impossible. However, she returned home one night from work to tell me the news. I had the delight, the joy and the ecstatic emotion of being told that she was indeed pregnant and there is not a feeling like it in the world, an indescribable euphoria.

What a high, what excitement, what anticipation and already my mind was filled with how we would prepare for our baby. 14 December was the date that is now indelibly imprinted in my mind I was the happiest man on the planet and immediately began planning for what lay ahead.

Will it be a boy or girl? What colour will we paint the nursery? I had so many exciting questions and I awaited the answers with proud and eager anticipation. Survivorship had given me the ultimate gift, the gift of bringing another life into the world.

Unfortunately, some twelve weeks later we lost our baby to a miscarriage and I found that trauma was harder to bear than my original cancer diagnosis. There was an emotional turmoil, nowhere to turn, tears followed tears, desperation and heartbreak, I had never known pain like it, my world had collapsed and my mind was filled with the thought of why life could be so cruel but I could not find an answer to that question.

To this day, the memory of that ill-fated period is as raw and emotive as the day it happened. My feelings and despair will forever remain a deep and personal secret. Inside my own mind, a deafening silence that would hide a million tears and a cascade of sadness lost in an unfulfilled paternal dream.

Despite the support shown by our friends and relatives, no one could stem the heartbreak and utter emotional distress June and I felt. The shadow of cancer had once again taken my emotions to an unknown low.

Family and friends were the supportive rocks during that very difficult time, ringing nightly to offer support and a shoulder to cry upon, but no support could lessen the psychological destruction caused by that single experience. Our house was a sad and quiet place, together, we cuddled, we cried and we tried to reflect. We had to accept that nature had intervened for a reason.

The cancer had attacked me with psychological turmoil and physical adversity that was unprecedented in my inexperienced life, yet this trauma was inflicted so unexpectedly and the hurt was unexplainable, intolerable and enough to break my heart. That experience is not something I would wish upon anyone and not one I would want to repeat.

Tests done months later by our doctor conclusively showed that my sperm, although low, had indeed regenerated. However, now into my sixties and with additional health problems, I had to accept that the reality of biologically having a son or daughter would not happen to me and it remains my greatest heartache.

Cancer has the ability to ensure that you reflect on every aspect of life generally, to see life without the pressure of conforming to mainstream views, to evaluate all that life has to offer and make your own decisions about it. It also causes you to reflect on your values and beliefs and, for me personally, I was confused about the dilemma of religion.

I had to admit that whilst religion is an important and powerful component to some people, it was not for me. The views expressed in this chapter are solely my views and are influenced by the experiences of what you have read so far. Importantly they are not expressed to offend or insult anyone else's views or opinions but to rationalise why I believe what I do.

In the same way that I do not judge anyone else on the grounds of religious belief, then equally I do not expect to be judged for the stance that I take. The ultimate questions we have all asked, and which have not yet been answered and probably never will be, is, what is the meaning of life. Where do we come from, why are we here, how did we get here and, of course, what about God, does he or she exist?

Phrase it how you wish, but it's a dilemma that has plagued each and every individual no matter what your cultural or religious beliefs are. When an individual is faced with a cancer diagnosis, the subsequent treatment and the inevitable doubt about mortality I am certain that many individuals would question their religious beliefs and that is perfectly understandable.

Ultimately, there is one final decision to make, you either believe or you do not. In fact, I think for those who do continue to believe, their faith is probably strengthened and may help them through the difficult time. For me, the faith I'd had before my and Donna's illness, went the way of scepticism.

I felt there were just far too many questions without answers and no concrete evidence that God exists. I accepted, even if I faced the prospect of a very early death, that fate had dealt me a risky hand of cards to play throughout my life, rather than it being God's will. Similarly, I could not reconcile that Donna's illness was part of God's plan; it made no sense to me whatsoever.

Furthermore, when I witness what happens around the world with poverty and disease, the cruelty of life generally and wars fuelled by religion, how I could possibly accept that somewhere there was a caring God; my mind was convinced that religion was simply a crutch for many or a blinkered view by many others.

However, I must emphasise that it would never be my position to criticise anyone else's views or opinions regarding religion, it is a personal choice based on experience. In theory, we are all made in the same vain and no individual is any better than any other and, as such, we owe it to one another to respect each other's individual values.

Sadly, the world doesn't operate in that fashion, we only have to look about the world to realise that man is his own worst enemy when it comes to respecting one another. The world is filled with destitution and poverty, prejudices and hatred, very often founded around religious beliefs, bitter and savage wars have been a significant part of man's history yet these are most often initiated by religion.

The so-called, holy war in the Middle East is a perfect example, a melting pot of religious hatred, a tinderbox of religious bigotry. The caring essence of religious philosophy was discarded in favour of confrontation and hostility. Catholics and Protestants have fought each other for hundreds of years in the name of religion, it happens all around the globe.

Wicked and unprecedented racism founded around religious doctrine, how can that be representative of religion, a so-called caring way of life? I just simply do not understand that. Different religions cannot even agree on the presence of a single God. It is a sad fact that we live in a fragmented world. I guess 9/11 is the prime example of hatred.

An attack of such magnitude and destruction that mere words could never describe the pain and torment it caused—all founded around an ideology of hatred that identifies the west as the enemy. And yet, just look at the unity that came from that dreadful assault. Admittedly, some people got their solace from their religion and I would never belittle that fact.

I suppose that's the weakness of mankind. The earth has been around for billions of years and thousands of Gods have been worshipped before the current one, who is to say that another won't take his or her place in the next millennium. There is no definitive proof that there is such a thing as God, yet people choose to believe it, in hope, but also in the fear of not being welcomed into his utopia.

I have little doubt that there was such a person as Jesus, yet the bible is littered with contradiction and I personally believe it has been grossly exaggerated over the years and much of this is to support the strength and hold that the church has over people. So many of the stories in the bible were written years, often hundreds of years, after the events they describe.

Religion does not encourage individuals to ask the questions I pose here, quite the contrary. Significantly and before my own and indeed, Donna's illness, I did believe in a God, although I was never a fervent supporter. I guess like so many, it was a fear of denouncing a God in case there was such an entity and the risk of being denied at the end of life.

For many, myself included, it is the experience of life that will mould personal or philosophical beliefs. If God is the creator of the earth, why is it that the planet is so unpredictable, where is his calming influence, his power? Violent earthquakes and hurricanes, tsunamis and weather out of our control and which most often affects the third world. That's a caring creator? Not in my view and ironically, these elements that are so destructive to innocent life are referred to as 'Acts of God'.

It is my understanding that religion is supposed to bring people together with a forgiving and compassionate ethos, yet the world over; religion proves divisive, confrontational and causes segregation across all of the different sects and beliefs. Shouldn't all religious believers be united and worship the same God or is that too simplistic?

Science can now explain and more importantly prove the origins of life and the evolution of the universe, formed by the merging of gases and minerals 13.8 billion years ago. Physics explains that within the universe there are many hundreds of different galaxies and many of these may be capable of supporting life.

To me, religion simply does not stand up to scrutiny and analysis. Life is too short for any approach other than mutual respect. Enjoy it while you can, for if you don't, one day, it'll be too late. That said, I do not intend to sound 'Holier than thou', nor do I believe that I am judgemental, I have my views and opinions on many things as we all do; neither do I think that any of my actions over the years have been taken in a deliberate attempt to hurt anyone.

I firmly believe that we are all entitled to the freedom of speech without fear of retribution. I live each and every day the only way I know, grateful for every day as it comes around knowing that I am fortunate to be alive and passionate about my music, my work and my family life; I love my wife unreservedly and look forward to the future ahead, although unsure as to what it holds.

My views expressed in this chronicle are not intended to upset or offend; they truly represent how cancer has manipulated my thought processes and ideals.

# Chapter 14
## Ten Seconds of Forever

My journey started with my musical discovery, none other than Hawkwind, but then led to a respect for the Lakota people and then the ultimate sick role as a cancer patient and my unparalleled psychological distress, followed by an unrivalled personal maturity, but also a realisation and sense of what life was all about, its beauty and innocence, its good points and also the bad aspects of life too, a character-building experience matched by no other.

An acknowledgement that as a cancer patient a coping mechanism was essential, everyone copes in different ways and Hawkwind and the Lakota Sioux proved to be my coping mechanisms and without them, I would have struggled. Equally and as importantly, my family were my building blocks of support.

Throughout the whole journey, I had discovered myself, someone I had not known until that moment. It then continued with the harsh and abrasive reality of being the parent of a child struck down by cancer, the destructive essence of coming close to losing your child to the predatory enemy of leukaemia, the desperation and helplessness that only a parent can know.

The joy and gratitude of survivorship from both perspectives and then the role of a student nurse and the ascendancy to Senior Haematology Nurse Specialist, a unique and most importantly, privileged rotation. I had travelled full circle, from the patient to the prescriber of chemotherapy, an ironic twist of fate.

But my life is not, by any stretch of the imagination, over yet it continues today, as the ever-youthful Hawkwind still actively tour on a regular basis, fuelling my travels around the country; travelling to a gig in Belfast and to the next in Manchester, from Newcastle to London and everywhere in between.

From 1975 to the present day, so many life-changing events have occurred and in many respects, it has been and continues to be, a fantastic journey, an ongoing journey of discovery, unmatched and unrivalled by any work of fiction and the realism of the cancer experience has impacted upon my own personal beliefs and philosophy changing my outlook on life forever.

But, I've now travelled three hundred and sixty degrees and although the future can never be seen as absolutely certain, my fate is already mapped out in front of me. What further surprises will surviving survivorship have in store for me and my shadow? Well, quite a few it seems.

Time stands still for no man and there is one important question that never goes away, particularly as the years march on, a question that frequently navigates my deep inner thoughts, even after almost fifty years and despite my own pragmatism or my own logical thought processes, the question remains, will it ever come back?

Perhaps it's because of the work that I do or possibly it is due to the new sense of security and happiness I have found with June that this question is now more prominent in my mind than ever before. 2004 was a significant year; in August I re-married and walked down the aisle to the sound of Hawkwind.

Then, at the annual Hawkwind Christmas concert at London's Astoria, I got an invite to the band's after-show party and, eventually, after a thirty-three year wait, I finally met and chatted with the man who for all that time had been my best friend, yet in all of that time I had never had the privilege of meeting; Dave Brock, founding member of Hawkwind.

In 2006, Hawkwind held a three-day festival at Donnington Park when I was invited onto the stage during their performance to recite Ten Seconds of Forever, a piece of work the band had written for their album Space Ritual back in 1972. However, I had re-written the lyrics to reflect the first ten seconds of a cancer diagnosis:

**In the tenth second of forever**
**I was informed that my world would end and with it my very existence**
**In the ninth second of forever**
**I felt a numbness overcome my body, the tingling sensation of fear and**
**the chronic pain of this reality**
**In the eighth second of forever**
**I thought of a leaf, a stone and the creaking branches of the ancient**
**oak tree and the innocence of life**
**In the seventh second of forever**
**I remembered an empty room where voices spoke to me about nothing**

**In the sixth second of forever**
**I thought of the life I would not lead and the effects of my confused**
**mind**
**In the fifth second of forever**
**I thought of the toxic poison that would attack my fragile veins**
**In the fourth second of forever**
**I could remember nothing I did not love**
**In the third second of forever**
**I thought of my Father, my Mother and my sister crying**
**In the penultimate second my diagnosis**
**I saw the rain caressing the window, the marshmallow clouds drift**
**through the sky**
**In the first and final second of what seemed forever**
**I thought of the others, those that had not been so fortunate and the**
**long past that had led to now**
**And never, never forever—**

It was an incredible experience in front of over 800 people and moreover, my wife June was at the side of the stage to see it. I received lots of compliments afterwards from people I did and did not know. Only a few months after my performance on stage with Hawkwind I plucked up the courage to ask the band's manager about joining the band on their next tour as part of the road crew, she pondered for less than a few moments and said yes.

Subsequently, I spent two tours (2007 & 2008) on the road with Hawkwind selling merchandise, unloading and setting up for gigs and stripping the stage after the gig was finished. I was on the road in the tour bus with other roadies and of course the band members. Fate can be a wonderful thing.

I was now musically inspired to form my own band, although I had never played an instrument in my life. I bought a synthesiser, then a keyboard, then another keyboard until eventually, I got Robin on guitar, Matt on Bass, Vince on vocals and Richard on drums.

Naturally, we played 'Space Rock' and were called 'Wind of Change'. As a result of my links with the band, we were invited to support Hawkwind at a three-day festival in Devon. Standing proudly on stage with my musical friends and hearing the sound of my keyboards echo through the air was a wonderful reflection of where I had been over the past few decades.

After three years of playing with 'Wind of Change,' the guys went off to pursue other musical interests while I was just getting started on a musical pathway and, therefore, I decided to continue as a solo artist, calling myself 'The Weird Noise Master' because of the sound I was aiming to create, a mixture of psychedelic rock combined with very early Pink Floyd with the added influence of Hawkwind.

I played locally for a few years until my good friend Alan Davey, who was perhaps one of the most influential bass players Hawkwind had ever had, invited me to support his band The Psychedelic Warlords on a national tour. Alan is one of the most talented musicians I know and is destined for mega-stardom in the near future.

After touring with Alan through England and Scotland I hung up my keyboards with a deep sense of satisfaction. Alan now lives near Death Valley and we remain good friends.

Yes, life was good, but then the timely reminder that I was still surviving survivorship came in late 2008. Following some routine investigations, the discovery of a tumour on my bowel wall took me by surprise. It was surgically removed and thankfully found to be benign.

But, the following year, I required a series of investigations which determined that as a consequence of the treatment given to me so many years earlier my Pituitary gland was now no longer functioning as it should, Hypopituitarism. The result of this underactive Pituitary gland is that my risk of osteoporosis, heart disease or even a brain tumour is a real threat to my mortality and consequently I now require daily hormone treatment, in addition to calcium and vitamin D supplementation.

In the same year, I discovered a small growth on my abdomen which after an investigation was found to be a secondary cancer caused by the salubrious Radiotherapy treatment I received way back in 1976; this was easily removed by surgical excision and never caused a problem again.

Later in 2009, my beloved Newcastle United endured relegation from the Premier league. Thankfully, they secured automatic promotion the following season. Meanwhile, in the same year, ex-England, and ex-Newcastle United manager (although he managed many other clubs, including the mighty Barcelona), and importantly all round lovely man, Sir Bobby Robson lost his fight with lung cancer.

Whilst I fully appreciated that I was enjoying survivorship the timely reminders that I was far from invincible and the treatment that was given decades earlier was still influencing my life. Following a rapid onset of breathlessness, a chest x-ray revealed that I had a condition called Pulmonary Fibrosis, a condition whereby the lungs are scarred and breathing is more difficult.

The respiratory consultant told me that this was caused by the Radiotherapy and may become more debilitating over the years; as a result, my inhaler is never far from reach!

Yet despite this legacy, I have achieved so many unexpected milestones and firmly believe that life truly is sweet and I realise that I am lucky to be here and appreciate each and every day as it happens. But I want more!

It is very true to say that we all need motivation in our lives and I was no exception. Hawkwind offered me their music which took me to another dimension and an abandonment of reality, an escapism that I required on many an occasion.

Yet, it was the Lakota Sioux who had inadvertently taken me under their 'Star Quilt' and comforted me like one of their own. My respect and admiration for a people so exploited, so maligned and so very nearly destroyed was a solace I will carry with me forever and is beyond my full appreciation.

Despite how much I enjoyed my work, my respect for life and an understanding that one day it will be my last, I decided in 2012 to take flexible retirement, reducing my hours to just twenty. Aware of my own health fragilities, retirement would allow me to enjoy the finer things in life; our grandchildren, fishing, photography and significantly travelling to America.

Travel, in particular, is so important for June and me, travelling to many corners of the world but especially America. So, as a reward to myself following retirement, we planned a three-week vacation to America; firstly to Arizona, taking in, naturally, the Grand Canyon, Tombstone and beyond. However, the trip would pinnacle with a visit to South Dakota, allowing me to at last visit Wounded Knee!

Unfortunately, my vocabulary does not have sufficient depth to describe what that meant. We had chosen a boutique bed and breakfast in Rapid City and the drive to Wounded Knee was a little over an hour. Leaving Rapid City that Tuesday morning the sun was cascading golden rays across the rolling hills taking us out of the City; as we drove across the vast Prairie, the overwhelming greenness delivered an atmospheric uniqueness that was so emotional.

A drive that was filled with anticipation but more importantly a drive of solitude and calm. Pulling off the road at Wounded Knee almost as soon as we got out of the car we were greeted by two Lakota natives, their wrinkled and sun-baked skin proof of whom they were, offering us the chance to buy their hand-made trinkets, whilst at the same time welcoming us to 'Wounded Knee' and making pleasant conversation.

Yet, they had no idea of who I was, where I had been, what I had experienced and significantly, what their history and culture meant to me.

After happily buying their gifts we bid them farewell and started our way along the red dusty path leading to the entrance of 'Wounded Knee Creek Cemetery' my anticipation of finally stepping foot onto such sacred ground gave me a tingle from the top of my spine all the way down to the bottom, goose bumps upon goose bumps.

'Wounded Knee' was all I had imagined, not a spectacular pasture, but definitely a serene and tranquil piece of history and yet in its own way, a paradise. Ancient graves with tattered wooden crosses were scattered here and there and headstones etched with names that I instantly recognised, including Chief Big Foot.

For me, having previously declared my rejection of religion, a strange feeling of spirituality was palpable and it was my honour to tread the sacred ground of the Lakota Oglala people and acknowledge those fallen warriors.

As I stood in that solemn field where, on 29 December 1890, three hundred and fifty men, women and children had been indiscriminately massacred by the seventh Cavalry, yet despite the poignancy and overwhelming sadness, this was a privilege I never thought I would experience; knowing that I was walking on the hallowed ground of the Lakota Sioux.

Since that initial visit, June and I have made that pilgrimage on many more occasions and until my dying day, I will never feel more comfortable there than on any other place on Earth, other than my own home of course. Surviving survivorship was, at last, paying some rewards.

2018 was a year of ups and downs. Forty-three years after being diagnosed with cancer, I decided to contact Pine Ridge Indian Reservation Council for permission to visit the reservation. After many messages back and forth I was eventually invited by a member of the council to spend the week on the Reservation as a guest of the Lakota Sioux.

My humble soul could not believe the offer and, needless to say, I accepted. Fate was now taking me from a young and definitely naïve adolescent supported mentally by the Sioux Nation and their sad history to physically being on their sacred land. My guide was Collins Gay, a Lakota Oglala native in his mid-fifties.

This trip I would make alone, a week spent travelling the length and breadth of the reservation, to places most white men have never been, including the grave of perhaps the greatest Lakota of all time, Chief Red Cloud. Pine Ridge Indian reservation is the poorest reservation in America with unemployment between 80 and 95%, life expectancy for a woman is just 52, while life expectancy for a man is a mere 48 years.

I encountered poverty as I have never seen before and yet the pride these people have is unrivalled. Yet, despite the obvious disparity, they called me brother and friend. Most importantly, they called me Wasi Chu—meaning non-native or 'white man'. On my last night on the reservation, I was asked to speak at the Oglala Sioux Tribe (OST) Council.

I thanked the members and in particular Collins but I was then flabbergasted, speechless and tearful when the Council presented me with a Star Quilt. The pattern of the quilt is inspired by the morning star which is the last and brightest star on the eastern horizon before dawn, the Lakota believed it represented the way the spirits came to earth and served as a link between the living and those who had passed.

Today, star quilts are one of the most valued gifts of the Lakota Sioux people and are still draped over the shoulders of the recipient to symbolise protection on their journey through life and are only bestowed upon honoured guests, although historically the quilts were draped around the shoulders of Lakota warriors and hunters when they returned from battle or a successful hunt. It was a truly poignant moment as in many respects I had been in a battle!

As I left the reservation that evening, Monday, 21 May 2018, ironically, exactly forty-three years to the day of starting chemotherapy, the sun setting in front of me, I was emotional, proud and humbled, but above all else, I promised myself that one day I would return to my friends of the Sioux nation on Pine Ridge Indian Reservation.

I now travel around the North of England and occasionally beyond giving talks about the Lakota Sioux, their history, their exploitation and their current plight.

Our trips to America continue and our family also continues to grow. Our greatest trip to the United States was undoubtedly a visit to Montana and I would conclude that if there were such as place as heaven, this is it and yet my biggest sadness is the fact that had I been twenty years younger and in better health, June and I have no doubt we would have emigrated to Livingston, Montana.

To date, we now have five grandchildren and one great-grandson. After Daniel, our youngest grandson, was born I would not realise just how significant he would be and the support he would unknowingly give me. Little did I realise, just how soon that support would be needed. We had decided upon a short vacation to Washington DC taking twenty-one-month-old Daniel with us.

The day before departing I had gone to the toilet and noticed a speck of blood in my urine. Clearly, this could be serious, then again it could be nothing so rather than interfere with our trip, I decided to make an appointment with my doctor for our return from DC and the following day we jetted off to America.

No more blood was seen until I went to the toilet on the aircraft and a red stream meant only one thing and I knew instantly what that was! Throughout our visit to DC I was passing blood on every occasion I went to the toilet although I was in no discomfort. My biggest concern was a major urinary problem whilst we were stateside and the potential financial burden that would incur.

Safely back home my GP made a two-week referral and I was seen at Newcastle Freeman Hospital, where a catheter was passed into my bladder to reveal a tumour. It would be a further three weeks before I found out whether it was benign or malignant.

Sadly, however, those three weeks were hell. Having removed the tumour from the bladder wall damage had been done to my prostate leaving me in agony, unable to pass water without discomfort and dependent upon strong painkillers, including liquid Morphine and that caused me to be constipated, which under the circumstances exacerbated my discomfort.

Three weeks later I presented myself to Freeman Hospital, knowing deep down in my consciousness what the result would show. During my treatment many years earlier I had received so much of a drug called Cyclophosphamide, which was known to be urotoxic that the one and only conclusion was bladder cancer.

It could be said that I was calmer for this consultation than any other in my life despite my expectation of the result. Given the treatment I had received, I knew I had an increased risk of secondary cancer, especially bowel, lung, leukaemia or even lymphoma.

Therefore, I felt that it could have been so much worse and, not wanting to be flippant or dismissive of the seriousness of any malignant diagnosis, bladder cancer is relatively easy to treat, if caught early—except for the embarrassment of the personal nature of the examination etc. And so in I went and the diagnosis I knew was coming was confirmed.

As for treatment, well the tumour had already been surgically removed and chemotherapy had been instilled into the bladder and that was all that was needed, other than repeated camera tests (cystoscopy) all of which to date have been clear. My journey on the road of surviving survivorship would continue.

Today, the prognosis for lymphoma and other cancers is more favourable than back in the seventies; however, we should remember cancer can and still claims lives today, including bladder cancer. Chemotherapy itself has become so much more refined and the side effects profile is far better than ever before, yet no matter, the navigation through chemotherapy remains a difficult one, both physically and, without fear of contradiction, psychologically.

Unfortunately, even in the modern health service today, there remains so much stigma and misconception around cancer and its valuable treatments, so many individuals expect or anticipate nothing but negativity and debilitating side effects when in reality, the dosages of drugs are calculated so much more carefully, which limits the toxicities.

The drugs available to prevent nausea and vomiting are so much more efficacious than ever before and the support from health care professionals, in most cases is now well established. Written information about all aspects of cancer management is accessible to all cancer patients should they require it, something unheard of forty-seven years ago?

Providing the written information allows individuals to make informed decisions, decisions that are right for them, but also to satisfy their need for at least some control. Significantly, a cancer diagnosis is an individual experience; it affects each and every one of us in a different way. But, the one solitary similarity, the single unification is that a diagnosis changes your perception of life forever.

Without a doubt, in my opinion, the cancer journey that I undertook all those years ago was not only a difficult road to navigate, but it also permitted me to mature personally, to respect and enjoy life and improve my own quality of life through reflection and appreciation.

Furthermore, the traumatic pain of witnessing Donna suffer at the hands of an impartial disease, indiscriminate in its choice of person, left me helpless to help my own child. But Donna's ability to adjust and learn to live with her disease and take from it positivism and that a cancer diagnosis does not automatically mean a death sentence, was pivotal and influential in my philosophy.

Therefore, cancer does not have to be a negative experience, despite the difficulty of coming to terms with it or the hardship of living with the disease, more support than ever before is available which is clearly a good thing. Importantly, I fully appreciate and respect the fact that not everyone diagnosed with cancer will be as fortunate as Donna and I were to be surviving survivorship, but hopefully, one day they will be.

When the cancer patient has completed treatment, they are seen at regular intervals in a clinic and the longer they stay in remission, the greater the time interval between clinics visits. If discharged from follow up, they are bound to suddenly feel more vulnerable due to an associated absence of support. Cancer patients, particularly long term survivors, are entitled to more support and the current system is changing to try and meet those demands.

Today, more and more individuals do survive the cancer experience, an acknowledgement of the advances medical science has made in respect to treatment approaches. As the survival curve becomes more acute then the health service needs to make provision for the psychological care requirements of those of us who are called survivors.

Communication is at the heart of psychological care and to deliver that fundamental aspect of care, professionals must learn to develop closer relationships with cancer patients. Following on from my diagnosis, it was clear that many nurses and doctors would actively distance themselves from cancer patients in fear of confronting their own mortality.

However, when Donna was diagnosed, the approach, although still far from perfect, was so much better than my experience in the seventies. Health care professionals, particularly the nurses would often communicate with honesty and sincerity no matter what question was asked, whether that question was asked by a child or a parent.

Cancer patients deserve to be supported through what is ultimately a challenge to their very existence; the most appropriate support health care providers can offer is through transparency and good communication that can increase the satisfaction of care and provide a trusting and emotional relationship.

Survivorship is sometimes just as difficult to deal with as the actual diagnosis, there is difficulty predicting what the future holds as cancer is such an unpredictable entity. The emotional fear that it evokes does not disappear, even after the all-clear has been given and in my opinion, psychological morbidity can debilitate an individual in the same way and occasionally worse than the physical symptoms activated by cancer and its unforgiving treatment.

Psychological support is such an important component of care for any cancer patient, that health care professionals ignore it at their peril. Psychological care is a lifelong need for cancer survivors; it needs to be a core component of the planned care pathway.

Today, my memory is not as good as it once was a hidden legacy of the beneficial treatment I received decades earlier. Many of us experience brain fog at some point in our lives - however, it is both a short-term and long-term consequence of chemotherapy and/or radiotherapy. It manifests as a feeling of tiredness or disorientation or a distraction, often, taking an extended period to fulfil a task or an inability to concentrate on a new skill.

The engines of emotion are constantly fuelled by my doubt and worry concerning my health and long-term survival. Yes, not a day goes by, when I do not fully appreciate how fortunate I am and, yet, it is a constant battle to control these emotions. Thankfully, I have June, who is my lifeline to normality; always there to up my glass.

Like all other individuals whose life has been affected by a cancer diagnosis, my journey was a unique one and yet it touched more than just my life, my diagnosis was not mine alone, it belonged to everyone important to me and it touched them almost as much as it touched me.

From those early days of my diagnosis and indeed, soon afterwards, it was thought that the entity that is lymphoma would terminate my existence, proving a totally destructive experience. The unequalled fear of losing Donna was an experience that simple words could not come close to describing. Yet, there is no doubt that my personal profile has been enhanced by the experience of a cancer diagnosis and as the parent of a child with cancer.

As for my support, June, the love of my life, is my number one passion; throughout my cancer journey and beyond, during my darkest moments, Hawkwind were there at the end of a stylus or in concert and the Lakota Sioux unknowingly gave me the spiritual support that only those indigenous natives could; however, my family were the rocks that I depended upon even though I wrongly hid so much from them.

So what has been my magical formula in life? Naturally, there is not one single factor or component that can claim to be the reason I overcame my cancer. For me as an individual, there were many reasons, not least of these was the support and love from my family and despite their attempts at misguided, but well-intentioned, collusion, I would not be here today without them.

The inspiration and time held dreams that Hawkwind gave me without taking anything in return; the doctors and nurses whose dedication and commitment to my cause was unswerving; my Lakota companions whom I knew personally but had never met. My friends who became an extension to my family, looking out for me and accepting and cajoling me through some dark moments, you all know who you are.

My positive mental attitude focussed my attention on the fact that this was a life-threatening illness and, yet, there were times when I was emotionally unstable and bereft of happiness as the positive mentality proved an impossible direction to steer. But almost paradoxically, I felt that unhappiness and depression was an important release valve.

Despite the urges of so many to insist and plead that I maintained the 'think positive attitude', it is sometimes easier said than done and I firmly believe that cancer patients are entitled to feel sorry for themselves from time to time. Significantly, I'm also sure that most, if not all would agree that a 'Positive mental attitude' is a major ingredient when it comes to fighting cancer.

In contrast, Donna's illness was so much harder to accept and contend with. My helplessness and sense of inadequacy when she needed me most was enormous, not knowing at that moment that what she was receiving throughout her cancer experience was something that could not be bought, love!

A transference of a sense of being wanted, being special and unique as all children are. Strangely, her reciprocation to me as her father gave her a purpose in life. Yet even so, throughout her illness, it was as if I was in a parallel universe unable to alleviate her suffering or ease her burden.

Everyone copes differently with a cancer diagnosis, no one element is above all others and my story is no different in that respect and as such, it is not intended to be prescriptive or a specific guide to others. It has allowed me to appreciate what many take for granted, to reflect on my own mistakes and there have been many and no doubt there will be many more.

Most importantly, it allowed me to discover myself and live life to the full and enjoy each and every day as it happened. One day will be my last and, therefore, I do not want to have any regrets about how I lived it. Even so, like everyone I still have dreams.

Take from my experience whatever you choose, criticise it where you feel necessary, but always remember that this was my experience of cancer as an individual, as a parent and now as a senior cancer nurse specialist. I truly believe it has made me the person I am today, a better person, philosophical, caring and determined to make a difference somewhere.

Moreover, when ultimately my time is at an end on this plane, my one wish is that I am heralded into the funeral service to a Lakota sound. A fitting tribute to what, in my opinion, has been a fulfilled existence.

In my nursing career, I have won many accolades both locally and nationally yet the gratitude of the patients I care for is worth more than any prize offered by the establishment and I know that I am very fortunate to be doing what I do, surviving survivorship and being part of the care of many patients with wide and varied haematological cancers.

Continuing on my highway of survival, what new challenges would cross my path? In 2020, forty-five years after my diagnosis, many more individuals became survivors; survivors of an international health crisis, Covid-19. A virus that ripped the heart out of our economy, divided families, prevented grandparents from seeing their grandchildren and created an untold mental health burden for thousands leading to an increase in suicide rates.

However, it also halted cancer treatments, which sadly contributed to mortality rates. It caused unprecedented psychological distress to thousands of cancer patients, who worried about their futures.

At the time of writing, an estimated 2.5 million people are living with cancer in the UK, this is anticipated to rise to four million by 2030; half of those individuals diagnosed with cancer in England and Wales will survive their illness for ten years or longer, which is great news – but we still need to strive for further survival success.

Cancer continues to be a leading cause of death in this country and with an ageing population means the incidence will continue to rise. Clearly, we now need a national initiative that can support the survivors of cancer and address the psychological needs that they will carry with them for the remainder of their lives.

# Chapter 15
# My Final Thoughts

The long pathway of life is fraught with obstacles; some large, some small, but all need to be jumped. When cancer knocked at my door, I had little idea how to deal with its psychological burden. The kaleidoscope of emotional turbulence caused my mind to spin out of control and I failed to manage my demons or the ongoing dark thoughts following repeated treatment failures. The incomparable side effects that almost destroyed my feeble frame are memories that have moulded my personality today. Never will I forget how fortunate I am.

I am humbled and honoured to have served as a senior haematology clinical nurse specialist, at the very top of the clinical nursing ladder and at the very hospital that established my cancer diagnosis over forty-seven years earlier. Ironically, I was the sole clinician performing bone marrow investigations at South Tyneside and every time I performed that procedure, I reminded myself of the time I was on the examination couch in 1975 about to undergo this same invasive but important procedure.

However, after almost thirty-three years working in Oncology and Haematology, I decided for several reasons, that the time was right to retire. My retirement brought sadness and I not only miss every component of my role but also influencing and being part of the care of so many incredible individuals, every one of them unique. Teaching nursing and medical staff on a whole range of cancer-related issues was also a real pleasure and an honour that I miss.

My health played a part in my final decision, as did the recent pandemic. In addition, with the change in management at South Tyneside NHS Foundation Trust, brought about when our hospital merged with another local Trust, I found the philosophy and approach towards staff changed and became so alien to what had gone before that I did not feel I wanted to be part of that new and unfriendly ethos.

Almost fifty years ago, I was the frightened patient, mentally scarred and physically feeble. Then, thirty-seven years ago; I was the father of a child diagnosed with leukaemia, terrified as to what lay ahead but, until only a few months ago, I was the nurse specialist, brimming with both confidence and pride—prescribing chemotherapy for those individuals with the same cancers as Donna and myself.

Truly a life-changing roller-coaster ride like no other, but I would not change it for the world as my fate was woven into the tapestry of life when John and Ruby announced the arrival of their son in 1957. On several occasions, I almost grasped the irreversible handshake that suicide offered me, but, without the courage to complete that task, I suddenly realised that life is so short; it is a precious commodity unknown in its content, dimension and significantly its length.

Life is not a rehearsal, it is for living, it is a once-only opportunity to enjoy. Our future is uncertain; no one knows what lies ahead, what fate has planned. Therefore, live life fully, enjoy it as if each day were your last, one day it will be and you should have no remorse to leave behind as I leave behind no remorse or regret. No one person can deny anyone else the opportunity to enjoy life to the best of their ability.

Never look back on your life unless you are prepared to smile and be reflective, never look forward unless you can dream—we all need dreams and we all need hope. Life can be cruel, often difficult to negotiate, as I and many others have discovered, but it's there to be enjoyed and it is our responsibility to do so.

That said, just being here, beating the odds is not without its challenges, as I have previously explained. I still endure moments when a cloak of darkness envelopes my thoughts and I am plunged into an unexplained low mood. I say unexplained because life presently could not be sweeter, family life is good, I can recommend retirement and I get to travel to America, at least once a year.

Yet, this unwanted plague of darkness occurs from time to time, even though June constantly tops up my glass and usually her eternal optimism and pragmatism is what gets me through. I still endure moments when blackness controls my sanity, thoughts of further health failures and worries about my mortality cloud my rational thought processes, thoughts that I cannot control.

There is little doubt, in my mind, that this psychological burden hails back to my early days of diagnosis and my parent's collusion in trying to hide my illness from me. But, more significantly, back in 1975, there was no Macmillan nurse; there was no clinical nurse specialist to support the cancer patient, a nurse who could demonstrate a high level of skill and knowledge.

These are complex roles, as I know only too well from my practice—these roles, however, had not been thought of in the seventies. Today, financial support packages are readily available to cancer patients; yet, these were non-existent during my illness—monetary support that can help support individuals with the hidden costs of a cancer diagnosis.

However, it is my view, that over and beyond financial support, psychological care is the fundamental element of help that can support patients to navigate the difficult pathway of cancer and its hidden network of obstacles. Sadly, it is my opinion, that some clinical nurse specialists lack the empathy and the knowledge to undertake these critical roles. A fact I have witnessed with "my" own eyes.

In today's modern NHS, the clinical nurse specialist should be working to empower individuals living with and beyond cancer. Patients should be supported as they adapt to life following the experience of prolonged and aggressive anticancer treatment that often can last years and which can be characterised by not insignificant acute and long-term toxicities.

In the past forty years, cancer survival rates have doubled. The survivors need support for both long-term health-related consequences of treatment but, also, their psychological morbidity.

The National Health Service is an unbelievable institution that we should be proud of and not take for granted. Cancer care has moved on since my diagnosis, not least with the emphasis on support and psychological care. It is not my intention to criticise the NHS. I have so much to thank it for, I am simply trying to identify why I remain troubled by the demons and memories of so long ago.

I truly believe it was that lack of support when both nurses and doctors were reluctant or refused to engage with the questions cancer patients asked about their disease and mortality. Of course, there will be other things that contributed, but that is a legacy I will take to my grave.

Surviving survivorship and becoming one of the longest-living cancer survivors is now the lifelong project that I continue to work on. In many respects, despite my advancing years, life is just getting going and I have so much more that I want to do and achieve. Who knows if I will have time to fulfil it all, but I intend to give it my best shot.

I am humbled, realising my good fortune to still be around today, talking of my experience, Life truly is sweet. At some point soon, I will re-visit Pine Ridge Indian Reservation and shake hands once again with the indigenous culture that inspired me to overcome societies greatest and perhaps most feared disease, cancer.

I will embrace the relatives of those that were my support throughout most, if not all, of my treatment and yet they had no idea of who I was. Visiting Wounded Knee again will also happen, of that, there is no doubt. Our ongoing excursions to America and the hinterland of Montana will continue which for June and me is heaven on earth.

Over the years, I have written dozens of articles for national and international nursing and medical press, presented lectures the length and breadth of the country on many aspects of haematology and cancer management. I am honoured to have won numerous awards both locally and nationally for my work in both oncology and haematology, yet, my greatest achievement is survival.

In 2021, Newcastle United were finally released from the stranglehold and fourteen-year ownership by a man who did not have the best interest of the club at heart – using the magpies to grow his financial empire. Hopefully, we, as long-suffering supporters can now look forward to the club moving forward with our new and visionary owners.

More recently and since retirement, I have started writing Children's fiction and my first two titles are now published—the first, *Strange Trips and Weird Adventures* was followed by *Blenkinsop Blabbermouth and the Ghost of Broderick McCaffery*. My third book, *The Fastest Water Pistol in Splodge City*, is waiting in the wings. All three are aimed at 7 to 11-year-olds and feature my grandson Daniel alongside yours truly.

But, the most important aspect of life is truly that of family, especially the grandchildren and we are blessed to have a supportive and loving network of family both here in England and beyond. Many people claim to have found their soul-mate, the love of their life I truly did. I am very fortunate that June is by my side and helping me to navigate the challenges of survivorship, including the lifelong psychological legacy it has bestowed upon me.

So, from clowning about at school to my love of rock music, from my initial steps onto the employment ladder to crashing down into a spiral of emotions following my cancer diagnosis, from the intolerable side effects leading to my contemplation of suicide to the euphoria of remission. Then, the catastrophic news that my daughter has leukaemia and the unimaginable helplessness of watching Donna suffer, to the elation of her unexpected remission.

The high of playing on stage at Donnington alongside members of Hawkwind, followed by my travels to South Dakota and Pine Ridge Indian Reservation and meeting the Lakota Sioux who helped me at the most difficult time imaginable. Moving from chronic ill health, including another cancer diagnosis, to my pride in delivering nursing care at my hometown hospital, the very hospital that established my diagnosis almost fifty years earlier, to my retirement and writing children's fiction. And so, my life goes on.

Nothing in this life is more important than family – they are a link to the past, and a connection to the future. One year before my father's death he told me that his father, my grandfather had told him during my illness that one day, he felt I would be a great man. Now, I could never be as great as either of them – grandad survived being captured by the Nazis, and was incarcerated as a prisoner of war during the First World War. Following his release, he returned to his family and worked the remainder of his life at Harton pit, as a miner. My father worked his entire life along the banks of the Tyne, and a kinder and more genuine man you could not wish to meet. But, if I died tomorrow, I can comfortably say, I have had a great life, but, I do not think or suggest that I am a great man.

Completing my memoirs has been a cathartic experience, but I hope, more importantly, readers will be able to take some solace and support from my story.

Finally, as the great wheel in the sky keeps on turning, no one knows where they will be tomorrow. But regardless of where that might be, my love and best wishes go out to you all, as I embark upon the next chapter in my life…